**HSE**
Health & Safety
Executive

# HEALTH AND SAFETY IN RETAIL AND WHOLESALE WAREHOUSES

HS(G)76

**Health and Safety Executive**

## Health and Safety in Retail and Wholesale Warehouses

ERRATUM

page 66  The classification for 'Corrosive substance' should read 'Class 8'.

December 1992
London: Her Majesty's Stationery Office

LONDON: HMSO

ISBN 0 11 885731 2

HS(G) series
The purpose of this series is to provide guidance
for those who have duties under the Health and
Safety at Work etc Act 1974 and other relevant
legislation. It gives guidance on the practical
application of regulations made under the Act, but
it should not be regarded as an authoritative
interpretation of the law.

Enquiries regarding this or any other HSE
publications should be made to the HSE Information
Centre at the following address:

HSE Information Centre
Broad Lane
Sheffield S3 7HQ
Tel: (0742) 892345
Fax: (0742) 892333

# CONTENTS

**Introduction** *v*

**Legal duties** *1*
Notifying the enforcing authority *1*    Informing employees *1*
Safety policy *1*    Relevant legislation *1*

**Staff training** *2*
General *2*    Training check-list *2*
Fitness for work *2*    Final check *2*

**Reporting accidents, diseases and other incidents** *3*
General *3*    Immediate notification *3*
Report in writing *3*    Record keeping *3*

**First aid** *6*
General *6*    Appointed persons *6*
Qualified first-aiders *6*    Contents of first-aid boxes *6*

**Environment and welfare** *7*
Design and layout *7*    Floors *7*    Heating *7*    Lighting *7*
Ventilation *8*    Gas and oil fired equipment *8*    Internal combustion engines *8*
Sanitary accommodation *8*    Washing and welfare facilities *8*    General housekeeping *9*
Personal protective equipment (PPE) *9*

**Electrical safety** *11*
General *11*    Fixed electrical installations *11*
Portable and transportable equipment *11*    Steam and water pressure cleaners *12*

**Occupational health** *14*
Substances hazardous to health *14*    Noise *16*
Work-related upper limb disorders *18*

**Storage systems** *20*
Pallets *20*    Turntable pallet stretch wrap machines *24*    Pallet inverters *26*
Pallet converters *26*    Trollies/roll containers *26*    Racking systems *27*
Placing and retrieving stock from racking or shelving *30*

**Manual handling** *31*
General *31*    Prevention or control of risk *31*
Team handling *33*    Information and training *34*
Check-list for employers *34*

**Mechanical handling** *35*
General *35*    Lift trucks *35*
Design features of reach, counterbalanced and very narrow aisle trucks *35*
Fitting attachments *36*    Training of lift truck operators *36*
Protection of public, employees and visiting drivers *37*
Lift truck operating areas *38*    Control of the use of LTs *39*
Basic rules for lift truck operators *39*
Maintenance and examination of LTs *39*    Refuelling of lift trucks *40*
Charging of batteries of electrically powered lift trucks *40*
Use of lift trucks where flammable materials may be present *41*
Working platforms on lift trucks *42*    Order picking machines *42*
Scissor lifts *44*    Conveyors *44*    Teagles *45*
Overhead travelling cranes *46*

**Automated storage and retrieval systems** *47*
General *47*  Hazards *47*
Automatic guided vehicles (AGVs) *47*
Hazard analysis and risk assessment *48*
Safeguarding automated and semi-automated systems *48*

**Vehicular operations** *51*
Road systems *51*  Pedestrian movement *51*
Protection of pedestrians working with vehicles *51*
Reversing vehicles *52*  Premature vehicle departure *53*
Stability of semi-trailers *53*  Loading and unloading *53*
Dock levellers *54*  Maintainence *54*
Tail lifts *54*  Safeguards *55*

**Cold stores** *56*
General *56*  Safeguards and precautions *56*

**Storage of packaged dangerous substances** *60*
General *60*  Identification and assessment *60*
Prevention and control strategy *60*  Spillages *61*
Warning signs *62*  Management and training *62*
Special regulations *62*

**Appendix 1** Enforcing authorities *64*
**Appendix 2** Routine electrical checks for portable apparatus *65*
**Appendix 3** Transport hazard diamonds and user hazard warnings *66*
**Appendix 4** Notes on fitness for work in the cold *68*
**Appendix 5** Further information sources *69*

# INTRODUCTION

1    This guidance is intended for owners and managers of retail and wholesale warehouses as well as the inspectors responsible for enforcing health and safety legislation in them. It will also be of value to employees and safety representatives. The principles set out here may also be applied to large retail outlets which have similar storage facilities and activities. The booklet briefly covers general health and safety matters and goes on to describe in detail the main risks associated with storage systems, manual and mechanical handling systems, equipment, substances and work practices which are found in warehouses. Good working practices and ways of safeguarding workers in the industry are suggested. Some warehouses undertake limited processes, such as the breaking down of bulk quantities into smaller units. This type of activity is also covered. The guidance has been produced by the Health and Safety Executive's Local Authority Unit after wide consultation with employers, trade unions and other interested organisations.

2    The Health and Safety Executive (HSE) is responsible for developing health and safety standards nationally. Local authorities are generally responsible for inspection and enforcement in most of these warehouses but some will fall to HSE for inspection and enforcement. Full details are given in Appendix 1.

3    The illustrations in the booklet are to assist in understanding the text and are not intended to represent any particular manufacturer's product.

4    While the information in this guidance is correct at the time of going to press, a number of directives from the European Community have recently been agreed and others are in preparation, which may require detailed changes to UK legislation.

5    A list of suggested information sources is given in Appendix 5. Further information and advice (including detailed advice on legal requirements) may be obtained from Local Authority Environmental Health Departments or from Area Offices of HSE.

## NOTIFYING THE ENFORCING AUTHORITY

6   Before employers can employ people to work in retail or wholesale warehouse premises they must serve notice on the appropriate enforcing authority (on Form OSR1) stating that people will be employed to work at the premises. See Appendix 1.

## INFORMING EMPLOYEES

7   An employer must either:

(a) display in a readable condition the approved poster (*Health and safety law - what you should know* - see Appendix 5); or

(b) give to each employee the approved leaflet (see Appendix 1).

8   The following information must be either clearly written on the poster, or given in writing to each employee:

(a) the name and address of the enforcing authority for the premises; and

(b) the address of the local Employment Medical Advisory Service (EMAS).

9   Under the Health and Safety at Work etc Act 1974 employers have a general duty to ensure, so far as is reasonably practicable, the health, safety and welfare at work of their employees and the health and safety of other people affected by their undertaking. This duty includes providing a safe and healthy workplace, safe machinery and safe systems of work, together with adequate information, instruction, training and supervision. Employees also have a duty to take reasonable care of their own health and safety and that of others.

## SAFETY POLICY

10   Businesses which employ five or more people should have a written statement of their policy for ensuring health and safety. This safety policy should help employers decide on priorities, detail health and safety objectives and outline the organisation that exists for ensuring they are met. It should also set out how the policy is to be implemented. For example when considering the use of lift trucks the policy will need to detail the dangers arising from their use, the system the company has for ensuring that only authorised, suitably trained and qualified people use them, what routine checks should be carried out, how often and by whom (see Mechanical Handling section).

11   The policy statement should be brought to the attention of all employees. Further advice can be found in the leaflet *Writing a safety policy statement* and the booklet *Writing your health and safety policy statement* (see Appendix 5).

## RELEVANT LEGISLATION

12   Specific requirements on health, safety and welfare in the workplace are also laid down in the following Acts and Regulations:

(a) the Factories Act 1961;

(b) the Offices Shops and Railway Premises Act 1963;

(c) the Electricity at Work Regulations 1989;

(d) the Control of Substances Hazardous to Health Regulations 1988;

(e) the Noise at Work Regulations 1989;

(f) the Protection of Eyes Regulations 1974;

(g) the Pressure Systems and Transportable Gas Containers Regulations 1989;

(h) the Highly Flammable Liquids and Liquefied Petroleum Gases Regulations 1972;

(i) the Reporting of Injuries and Dangerous Occurrences Regulations 1985;

(j) the Health and Safety (First-Aid) Regulations 1981;

(k) the Safety Representatives and Safety Committees Regulations 1977;

(l) the Fire Precautions Act 1971;

(m) the Control of Major Accident Hazards (CIMAH) Regulations 1984;

(n) the Dangerous Substances (Notification and Marking of Sites) Regulations 1990;

(o) the Food and Environment Protection Act 1985;

(p) the Control of Pesticides Regulations 1986;

(q) the Safety Signs Regulations 1980.

13   All this safety legislation may apply to warehouses. In some premises other health and safety regulations may also apply. For example, where dangerous substances are sent from a warehouse by road, the Road Traffic (Carriage of Dangerous Substances in Packages etc) Regulations 1986 may apply. For further information on general legal requirements see the HSE publication *Essentials of health and safety at work* (see Appendix 5).

LEGAL
DUTIES

1

## GENERAL

14 Many accidents occur when employees, particularly young employees, use machines, equipment, substances or work in hazardous circumstances without proper training. No one should use dangerous equipment or substances unless they have been properly trained and are competent. Managers and supervisors will also need suitable training and should be competent.

Information and advice for training may be obtained from:

(a) the supplier of the material, substance or equipment;

(b) training centres or colleges of further education;

(c) trade associations;

(d) trade unions;

(e) the Health and Safety Executive;

(f) Local Authority Environmental Health Departments;

(g) professional bodies (for example the Institution of Occupational Safety and Health);

(h) voluntary bodies (for example the Royal Society for the Prevention of Accidents, the British Safety Council).

## TRAINING CHECK-LIST

15 The following check-list shows what needs to be considered when preparing a typical training programme:

### Organisation

- Will training be 'on' or 'off' the job?

- Who will do the training? (Will they be competent?)

- Who will supervise the training? (Will they be competent?)

- How will the trainees' competence be assessed?

- What will the trainee be competent in at the end of the training?

- What records will be kept?

- Who will keep the records?

### Selecting and assessing the trainee

- How is the trainee to be selected? Selection should take account of the physical and mental demands of the job.

- How much does the trainee know already about safe working practices?

### Basic instruction

For each task prepare a list of all the points training should cover, for example:

- what the method of work is;

- what equipment or substance to use;

- how the equipment or substance works and what it does;

- what dangers are associated with its use, including accidental spillage;

- what safety precautions are needed and how they protect the user;

- how to clean equipment safely;

- what to do if equipment seems faulty; and

- what personal protective equipment to wear.

### Supervised working

- Make sure the supervisor is competent for the training task.

- Set the trainee to work under close supervision.

- Make sure the supervisor has the time and knowledge to supervise effectively.

- Make sure the supervisor watches closely to see that dangerous practices do not develop.

## FITNESS FOR WORK

16 People's physical capacities vary. Some tasks, for example lift truck driving or working in cold stores, place particular physical demands on workers, and individuals need to be specially selected and trained for these jobs. Other people may have health problems which affect their ability to do more normal jobs. Many employees find their capacity for work temporarily reduced by illness or injury. Those returning to work after a period of sickness are likely to need help in readjusting to their jobs. Workers must be physically and mentally suited to their jobs. It is usually possible to anticipate and resolve problems by seeking specialist advice.

## FINAL CHECK

17 Check that trainees know how to carry out the work properly and safely. Make sure they can be left to work safely without close supervision and monitor performance on a regular basis.

STAFF
TRAINING

2

## GENERAL

18   Under the Reporting of Injuries, Diseases and Dangerous Occurrences Regulations 1985 (RIDDOR) employers have a legal duty to report certain accidents, dangerous occurrences and occupational diseases to their enforcing authority.

## IMMEDIATE NOTIFICATION

19   Employers should notify their enforcing authority (see Appendix 1) as soon as possible, normally by telephone, if:

(a)   someone dies or suffers a major injury in an accident connected with their business;

(b)   an employee is injured which results in immediate hospital admission for more than 24 hours;

(c)   there is a dangerous occurrence.

## REPORT IN WRITING

20   Employers should send a report to their enforcing authority within seven days if:

(a)   an employee is off work or cannot carry out normal duties for more than three days as a result of an accident at work;

(b)   any death, major injury or dangerous occurrence has previously been notified by telephone;

(c)   a specified occupational disease is certified by a doctor.

21   Reports should be made on Form 2508 for accidents and dangerous occurrences (a reduced copy of Form 2508 is shown in Figure 1). Form 2508A should be used for reporting cases of disease. These forms are available from HMSO bookshops (see back cover for details). Photocopies of the forms may be used. The HSE booklet *Reporting an injury or dangerous occurrence* (see Appendix 5) gives further advice on the requirements of RIDDOR.

## RECORD KEEPING

22   Employers should keep a record of any reportable accident, dangerous occurrence or case of disease. These records should include:

(a)   date and time of accident or occurrence;

(b)   name, occupation and nature of injury of person affected;

(c)   place where incident happened; and

(d)   a brief description of the circumstances.

REPORTING ACCIDENTS

3

HSE
**Health & Safety Executive**

*Health and Safety at Work etc Act 1974*
*Reporting of Injuries, Diseases and Dangerous Occurrences Regulations 1985*

Spaces below
are for office
use only

# Report of an injury or dangerous occurrence

- Full notes to help you complete this form are attached.
- This form is to be used to make a report to the enforcing authority under the requirements of Regulations 3 or 6.
- Completing and signing this form does not constitute an admission of liability of any kind, either by the person making the report or any other person.
- If more than one person was injured as a result of an accident, please complete a separate form for each person.

**A   Subject of report** *(tick appropriate box or boxes)* — *see note 2*

| Fatality ☐ 1 | Specified major injury or condition ☐ 2 | "Over three day" injury ☐ 3 | Dangerous occurrence ☐ 4 | Flammable gas incident (fatality or major injury or condition) ☐ 5 | Dangerous gas fitting ☐ 6 |

**B   Person or organisation making report** (ie person obliged to report under the Regulations) — *see note 3*

Name and address —

Post code — ☐

Name and telephone no. of person to contact — ☐

Nature of trade, business or undertaking —

If in construction industry, state the total number of your employees — ☐

and indicate the role of your company on site *(tick box)* —

| Main site contractor ☐ 7 | Sub contractor ☐ 8 | Other ☐ 9 |

If in farming, are you reporting an injury to a member of your family? *(tick box)*   ☐ Yes   ☐ No

**C   Date, time and place of accident, dangerous occurrence or flammable gas incident** — *see note 4*

Date ☐ ☐ 19 ☐
*day  month  year*

Time — ☐

Give the name and address if different from above —

Where on the premises or site —
and
Normal activity carried on there

ENV ☐

Complete the following sections D, E, F & H if you have ticked boxes, 1, 2, 3 or 5 in Section A. Otherwise go straight to Sections G and H.

**D   The injured person** — *see note 5*

Full name and address —

Age ☐   Sex ☐ (M or F)

Status *(tick box)* —

| Employee ☐ 10 | Self employed ☐ 11 | Trainee (YTS) ☐ 12 |
| Trainee (other) ☐ 13 | | Any other person ☐ 14 |

Trade, occupation or job title —

Nature of injury or condition and the part of the body affected —

F2508 (04/92)

*continued overleaf*

**Figure 1**  Sample copy of Form 2508

REPORTING
ACCIDENTS

**4**

## E  Kind of accident - *see note 6*

Indicate what kind of accident led to the injury or condition (*tick one box*) —

| | | | |
|---|---|---|---|
| Contact with moving machinery or material being machined ☐ 1 | Injured whilst handling lifting or carrying ☐ 5 | Trapped by something collapsing or overturning ☐ 8 | Exposure to an explosion ☐ 12 |
| Struck by moving, including flying or falling, object. ☐ 2 | Slip, trip or fall on same level ☐ 6 | Drowning or asphyxiation ☐ 9 | Contact with electricity or an electrical discharge ☐ 13 |
| Struck by moving vehicle ☐ 3 | Fall from a height* ☐ 7 | Exposure to or contact with a harmful substance ☐ 10 | Injured by an animal ☐ 14 |
| Struck against something fixed or stationary ☐ 4 | *Distance through which person fell ☐ (metres) | Exposure to fire ☐ 11 | Other kind of accident (give details in Section H) ☐ 15 |

Spaces below are for office use only.

☐

## F  Agent(s) involved — *see note 7*

Indicate which, if any, of the categories of agent or factor below were involved (*tick one or more of the boxes*) —

| | | | |
|---|---|---|---|
| Machinery/equipment for lifting and conveying ☐ 1 | Process plant, pipework or bulk storage ☐ 5 | Live animal ☐ 9 | Ladder or scaffolding ☐ 13 |
| Portable power or hand tools ☐ 2 | Any material, substance or product being handled, used or stored. ☐ 6 | Moveable container or package of any kind ☐ 10 | Construction formwork, shuttering and falsework ☐ 14 |
| Any vehicle or associated equipment/ machinery ☐ 3 | Gas, vapour, dust, fume or oxygen deficient atmosphere ☐ 7 | Floor, ground, stairs or any working surface ☐ 11 | Electricity supply cable, wiring, apparatus or equipment ☐ 15 |
| Other machinery ☐ 4 | Pathogen or infected material ☐ 8 | Building, engineering structure or excavation/underground working ☐ 12 | Entertainment or sporting facilities or equipment ☐ 16 |
| | | | Any other agent ☐ 17 |

Describe briefly the agents or factors you have indicated —

## G  Dangerous occurrence or dangerous gas fitting — *see notes 8 and 9*

Reference number of dangerous occurrence ☐        Reference number of dangerous gas fitting ☐

## H  Account of accident, dangerous occurrence or flammable gas incident - *see note 10*

Describe what happened and how. In the case of an accident state what the injured person was doing at the time —

Signature of person making report _____        Date _____

## GENERAL

23   Under the Health and Safety (First-Aid) Regulations 1981 warehouses should have first-aid provision. The form it should take depends on various factors, including the nature and degree of the hazards at work, what medical services are available, and the number of employees. The HSE booklet *First aid at work* contains an Approved Code of Practice and guidance notes to help employers meet their obligations (see Appendix 5).

## APPOINTED PERSONS

24   The minimum requirement for any workplace is that at all times when people are at work, there should be at least one person appointed who will take charge of an emergency situation and the first-aid equipment in the absence of a qualified first-aider. It is recommended that an appointed person should have received emergency first-aid training.

## QUALIFIED FIRST-AIDERS

25   In warehouses where there is likely to be substantial use of dangerous plant and machinery, for example overhead travelling cranes, lifting machinery and conveyor systems, substantial risk from handling dangerous substances or special risks from handling stored products, for example glass, it is recommended that at least one qualified first-aider is provided. A qualified first-aider is a person who has undergone training and obtained qualifications approved by HSE.

## CONTENTS OF FIRST-AID BOXES

26   First-aid box(es) should be provided and should contain only items that a first-aider has been trained to use. It should not contain medication of any kind. It should always be adequately stocked. A list of contents is shown in Table 1. Notices should be displayed giving the location of first-aid equipment and the name and location of the first-aider or appointed person.

27   All cases dealt with should be recorded by the first-aider or appointed person. Records should include at least the name of the casualty, date, time and circumstances of the incident with details of the injury sustained and any treatment given. Employees or their representatives may wish to inspect these records at any time. Records should therefore be kept in a suitable place where they are easily available for inspection.

**Table 1** Contents of first-aid boxes and kits

| Item | First-aid boxes | Travelling first-aid kits |
|---|---|---|
| Guidance card | 1 | 1 |
| Individually wrapped sterile adhesive dressings (assorted sizes) | 20 | 6 |
| Sterile eye pads, with attachment | 2 | |
| Individually wrapped triangular bandages | 6 | 2 |
| Safety pins | 6 | 2 |
| Medium sized individually wrapped sterile unmedicated wound dressings (approx 10 cm x 8 cm) | 6 | |
| Large sterile individually wrapped unmedicated wound dressings (approx 13 cm x 9 cm) | 2 | 1 |
| Extra large sterile individually wrapped unmedicated wound dressings (approx 28 cm x 17.5 cm) | 3 | |
| Individually wrapped moist cleaning wipes | | |

## DESIGN AND LAYOUT

28 Warehouse design and layout should take account of the following:

(a) people and vehicles should be segregated as far as is reasonably practicable. Traffic routes internally and externally should be clearly defined and conspicuously marked. One-way traffic systems should be considered (see paragraph 224);

(b) emergency exits should be clearly marked, easily and immediately openable and should always remain unobstructed and readily accessible. Wherever possible and in all cases from areas of high fire risk, emergency exits should open in line with the route of exit;

(c) where lift trucks and other vehicles are used, areas should be flat and unobstructed; awkwardly sited doors or tight corners should be avoided as far as possible;

(d) storage areas and gangways should be clearly marked out on the floor, including floor markings where necessary. Gangways should be wide enough to ensure that mechanical handling equipment can be easily manoeuvred;

(e) external doorways used by mechanical handling equipment should be protected from adverse weather conditions, by for example hinged rubber doors with vision panels, plastic strip curtains;

(f) staircases and ramps used for pedestrian access should be provided with suitable handrails;

(g) access to automated areas should be strictly controlled, for example interlocked access routes, permit-to-work systems (see Automated Storage of Retieval Systems section).

## FLOORS

29 Floors should be capable of bearing the general overall load to which they may be subjected and any point loading from stock either with or without pallet racking. Further information on floor loading can be found in the Building Research Establishment Report *Floor loading in warehouses - review* (see Appendix 5). Floors should be constructed and designed to withstand the use to which they may be subjected, for example physical damage from lift trucks and wheeled equipment, corrosion from chemical substances. Mezzanine floors should be clearly and conspicuously marked with their safe load bearing capacity. Where personnel are allowed access, all openings and edges of the floor should be guarded to prevent any

goods or people falling and a safe means of access must be provided. It is particularly important that any sections of the guard which are removable for loading, for example by lift truck, are replaced as soon as loading is complete. A system of guarding is available which allows goods to be transferred to and from mezzanine floors while maintaining adequate protection against falls.

## HEATING

30 Effective provision should be made for heating and maintaining a reasonable temperature in all workrooms. Permanently installed room sealed appliances, such as those with balanced flues, provide the best method of heating. Whatever method is used, it should be of a design that prevents the escape of any harmful or offensive fumes into the workroom. Where it is not practicable to provide and maintain a reasonable temperature, for example when loading bay doors are required to be constantly open or where low temperature storage is an absolute requirement (cold storage of perishable food stuffs), there should be provided at conveniently accessible places effective means of enabling employees to warm themselves, for example a heated messroom. Employees should be given reasonable opportunities to use such facilities.

31 It is expected that legislation to implement EC directives will lead to an Approved Code of Practice which will contain guidance on providing a reasonable temperature at work.

## LIGHTING

32 Good lighting, whether natural or artificial, is vital in promoting health and safety at work. In all working and access areas sufficient lighting should be provided to enable work activities to be carried out safely. The level and type of lighting depends on:

(a) the type of work being carried out;

(b) the hazards associated with it.

Recommended illuminances for different areas of a warehouse are given in Table 2.

33  In warehouses there can be considerable obstruction to lighting, for example from racking. It is therefore important to arrange lighting to avoid shadows (see Figure 2).

**Table 2** Average illuminances and minimum measured illuminances for different areas of a warehouse

| Area of warehouse | Average illuminance: lux | Minimum measured illuminance: lux |
|---|---|---|
| Loading bays | 50 | 20 |
| Shelves/racking | 100 | 50 |
| Offices | 200 | 100 |

Notes:

1  Average illuminance is for the work area as a whole.

2  Minimum measured illuminance is the minimum permitted at any position within the work area.

3  Where the work or task is predominantly on one plane or vertical, the recommended illuminances are intended for that plane.

Further details can be found in the HSE guidance booklet *Lighting at work* (see Appendix 5).

## VENTILATION

34  Generally, most warehouses where loading/unloading doors are open during the working day will not usually require any special ventilation arrangements. However, specific ventilation requirements may be necessary for the storage of some materials or where combustion equipment (see paragraphs 36-37) is used inside the warehouse. A warehouse containing combustion equipment or plant, such as oil or gas fired heaters and lift trucks with internal combustion engines, will require air for the combustion process and, if the plant or equipment is not flued, to dilute toxic combustion products (carbon monoxide, carbon dioxide and oxides of nitrogen) to an acceptable level.

## GAS AND OIL FIRED EQUIPMENT

35  Fresh air requirements for gas and oil fired equipment will depend on whether the equipment is open flued (drawing air from the room and discharging combustion products to the atmosphere), room sealed (drawing air from and discharging combustion products to the atmosphere) or flueless (drawing air from and discharging products to the room). If ventilation is inadequate, carbon monoxide levels can increase rapidly, increasing the danger of carbon monoxide poisoning from unflued combustion equipment.

Note: Unflued space heaters are not recommended. Room sealed appliances are recommended where ventilation is difficult.

## INTERNAL COMBUSTION ENGINES

36  Lift trucks (LTs) powered by internal combustion engines (petrol, diesel, liquified petroleum gas (LPG)) emit toxic exhaust gases and particulates. If these trucks are used inside a warehouse it may be necessary to provide adequate ventilation to remove exhaust fumes. Ventilation requirements will vary according to:

(a) the number of LTs used;

(b) the volume of the warehouse or LT operating area;

(c) the type of fuel used (for example petrol engines emit more carbon monoxide than diesel or LPG engines);

(d) the condition of the engine (proper engine maintenance will reduce toxic emissions).

37  In some situations, for example where large numbers of LTs powered by internal combustion engines are used, it may be that the risk assessment under the Control of Substances Hazardous to Health Regulations (COSHH - see paragraphs 63-78) will indicate the need for action to reduce the risk.

Note: LTs powered by internal combustion engines of any type should not be used in any workspace where the lack of ventilation would lead to a build-up of toxic fumes.

## SANITARY ACCOMMODATION

38  Suitable and sufficient sanitary conveniences should be provided for employees. In most warehouses this will mean at least one WC should be provided for each sex. Where more than 15 employees of each sex are regularly employed at any one time additional WCs must be provided. It is expected that legislation to implement EC directives will in future allow, as an alternative to separate toilets for men and women, one or more unisex facilities used by one person at a time behind a locked door.

Sanitary conveniences should be:

(a) kept clean and properly maintained;

(b) well ventilated and lit and not communicating directly with a workroom;

(c) undercover, partitioned off for privacy with suitable doors and fastenings;

(d) readily accessible from workrooms;

(e) so screened that urinals are not visible when the door to the room is open.

## WASHING AND WELFARE FACILITIES

39  Washing facilities should be provided which are both adequate and suitable. At least one wash basin

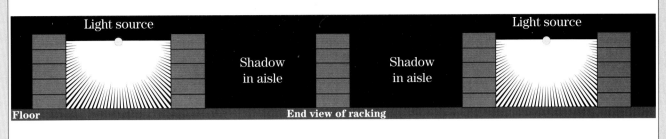

**Figure 2(a)** Uneven distribution of lighting with shadows

Light source       Light source

Shadow in aisle      Shadow in aisle

Floor      End view of racking

**Figure 2(b)** Even distribution of lighting without shadows

Light source    Light source    Light source    Light source

No shadow in aisle     No shadow in aisle

Floor      End view of racking

should be provided for each WC. In some warehouses, for example where dirty materials or substances are handled, more wash basins will be required. Washing facilities should be:

(a) kept clean and properly maintained;

(b) provided with running hot and cold water together with soap or other proprietary hand cleaner and suitable drying facilities;

(c) provided at convenient locations that are sufficiently lit.

Drinking water should be provided at conveniently accessible points, which should not be within a toilet cubicle or close to a urinal.

40 Suitable accommodation for clothing not worn at work should be provided together with suitable drying facilities. For example, there should be sufficient coat hooks in a clean, dry and well ventilated place.

41 Suitable facilities, for example a heated and adequately lit room with a sink, hot and cold water, tables and chairs, should be provided for employees to use during meal and tea breaks.

## GENERAL HOUSEKEEPING

42 Many accidents at work are caused by people tripping over things left on the floor or slipping on spillages. Work areas, offices, messrooms, storage areas, aisles and gangways, washing and toilet facilities should be kept clean and tidy at all times:

(a) stock or other items should not be allowed to project or accumulate in aisles and gangways;

(b) spillages should be cleaned up immediately;

(c) suitable signs should be displayed when the floor is being washed.

## PERSONAL PROTECTIVE EQUIPMENT (PPE)

43 PPE includes both:

(a) protective clothing such as overalls, waterproof equipment, gloves, safety footwear, helmets etc;

(b) protective equipment such as eye protectors and ear protectors.

PPE should not be used as a substitute for other methods of risk control. It should always be regarded as a 'last resort' means of preventing or controlling exposure to hazards to safety and health. This means that other methods of controlling exposure must be considered before taking the decision to use PPE. In some situations, however, it will be necessary to provide protective clothing and/or equipment.

44 Selection of PPE should take into account the demands of the job. Among other things, this will involve considering the physical effort required to do the job, the methods of work, how long the PPE needs to be worn and requirements for visibility and communication. The aim should always be to choose equipment which will give minimum discomfort to the wearer. Uncomfortable equipment is unlikely to be worn properly.
There will be considerable differences in the physical dimensions of different workers and therefore more than one type or size of PPE may be needed. There is a better chance of PPE being used effectively if it is accepted by each wearer. Those having to use PPE should therefore be consulted and involved in the selection and specification of the equipment.

**Table 3** Protective clothing

| Function | Hazards | Choices |
|---|---|---|
| Eyes | Chemical splash, dust, projectiles. | Spectacles, goggles, face screens (to BS 2092). |
| Head and neck | Impact from falling or flying objects, risk of trips, head bumping, trips, adverse climate or temperature. | Helmets (to BS 5240), sou'wester, insulated head covering (insulated hooded jackets). |
| Hearing | Impact noise, high intensities. | Earplugs, ear protectors (to BS 6344 - see paragraphs 93-99) |
| Hands and arms | Abrasion, temperature extremes, cuts and punctures, chemicals, skin contamination. | Gloves,[1] gauntlets, mitts (to BS 1651). |
| Feet and legs | Wet, slipping, cuts and punctures, falling objects, abrasion, crushing. | Safety boots and shoes with steel toe caps and steel mid-sole, gaiters, leggings (to BS 1870), non-slip footwear. |
| Respiratory system | Toxic and harmful dust, gases and vapours. | Disposable respirators, half or full face mask respirators fitted with filtering cartridge or canister, powered respirators, fresh air hose equipment, self-contained breathing apparatus[2]. |
| General body | Heat, cold, bad weather, chemical splash, spray from pressure equipment | Overalls (conventional or disposable), boiler suits, warehouse coats, donkey jackets, thermal or insulated clothing, water proof suits[3] |

**Notes:**

1 Gloves must never be worn when operating machines where they might get caught. Some materials are easily penetrated by particular chemicals: care in selection is needed.

2 All equipment should be suitable for its purpose and should conform to an HSE approved standard or be type approved by HSE.

3 High visibility clothing to BS 6629: see Vehicular Operations section

PPE provided by an employer or self-employed person after 30 June 1992 must carry a CE mark which certifies that it satisfies the wide ranging safety requirements stipulated in the EC Product Directive.

45 Before purchasing and issuing equipment consider the following points:

(a) choose good quality products made to a recognised or approved standard;

(b) choose equipment which is suitable for the person using it and is appropriate for the hazard;

(c) make sure the user is properly trained in the use, fitting and basic maintenance of the equipment and instructed to report defects;

(d) make sure the user knows why the equipment is needed, when and how it has to be used and its limitations;

(e) equipment needs to be kept clean and in good repair. Suitable storage facilities should be provided.

46 In warehouses where particular hazards (see Table 3) exist protective clothing/equipment should be provided.

## GENERAL

47  All electrical equipment and electrical systems installed and used at warehouse premises are subject to the Electricity at Work Regulations 1989. Guidance on how to comply with these Regulations is given in the *Memorandum of Guidance on the Electricity at Work Regulations 1989* (see Appendix 5). Electricity can not only cause shock, but can also cause burns and start fires. It should therefore never be treated lightly. All electrical equipment and systems within work premises should be installed and maintained by a competent person (in most instances this will be a qualified electrician).

48  Where conditions are wet, only electrical equipment suitable for that environment should be used. Guidance to appropriate IP (Index of Protection) ratings may be found in BS 5420, BS 5490 and IEC (International Electro-Technical Commission) 529 2nd Edition. Where flammable liquids, gases or combustible dusts are stored, all electrical installations and equipment, including powered handling equipment, should be suitable for use in the environment.

## FIXED ELECTRICAL INSTALLATIONS

49  All fixed electrical installations should be designed, installed, operated and maintained (including being inspected and tested) in accordance with the current edition of the Regulations for Electrical Installations, published by the Institution of Electrical Engineers (the IEE Wiring Regulations).

50  Where flammable solvents, liquids or flammable gas containers are stored, specialist advice is required in relation to the electrical installation and equipment to be installed. Guidance may be found in BS 5345. Where combustible dusts are stored, for example flour, corn starch etc, specialist advice will again be required. Guidance may be found in BS 6467.

51  The electrical wiring should be protected against mechanical damage. This can be achieved by using PVC insulated wires in conduit or trunking or by PVC steel-wire armoured cable with an outer PVC sheath. Each machine supplied via a permanent cable should have its own switch suitable for electrical disconnection and isolation from the electrical supply. This switch should be provided with a means to secure it in the 'off' position. This switch should always be used to disconnect the machine and be secured in the 'off' position before cleaning and maintenance work. For further information consult the HSE Guidance Note *Electricity at work: safe working practices* (see Appendix 5). 'Start' buttons should be recessed or shrouded to prevent unintended operation, while 'stop' buttons should be coloured red and protrude for easy operation. They should be within easy reach of the operator.

52  In line with the IEE Wiring Regulations, it is recommended that the fixed electrical installation should be tested at least once every five years by a competent person. He or she should advise of any defects, carry out the necessary remedial work or isolate the system or part of the system which is defective and prepare a certificate once satisfied.

53  All electrical switchgear controlling machinery should be clearly and unambiguously labelled and identified to indicate which machine is controlled by which switchgear. All switchgear should be readily accessible at all times. Goods etc should not be stored in front of or obstruct access to switchgear.

## PORTABLE AND TRANSPORTABLE EQUIPMENT

54  Work areas should have sufficient socket outlets to avoid the use of adaptors and trailing cables across floors. Industrial types of plugs and sockets (complying with BS 4343) should be used. Where a number of pieces of equipment require electrical supplies in the middle of the work area, consider the provision of overhead sockets. These sockets should be readily reached and be accessible to those who are to use them.

55  All flexible cables should be suitable for their environment. You may require specialist advice as to which cable is most suitable for your premises, for example flexible cables for floor cleaning equipment should be abrasion resistant, for example pcp (polychloroprene) sheathed or similar.

56  Appropriate electrical protection should be provided for all portable and transportable electrical equipment. This protection may take the form of a suitably rated fuse either at a distribution fuseboard in a fixed installation or in a plug top designed for that purpose or alternatively by a suitably rated circuit breaker at the distribution switchboard for a fixed installation.

57  Efficient cable or cord grips should be used both at the plug and where the cable enters the equipment. Cables should be positioned and protected so that they cannot be damaged by heavy equipment or materials and should be checked regularly for any signs of damage. Damaged cables should generally be replaced completely but, if they are repaired, this should be by means of a suitable coupler.

ELECTRICAL
SAFETY

11

Never carry out makeshift repairs to cables. Further information is available in the HSE Guidance Note *Flexible leads, plugs, sockets etc* (see Appendix 5).

58  Where electrical equipment, flexible cables, plugs and sockets are likely to be used outside or in wet conditions, the equipment, cables, plugs and sockets should be suitable for that use, ie use BS 4343 industrial type plugs and sockets, or, for very wet conditions, connectors with an IP rating not less than IP 56.

59  All extension cables which are terminated in conventional 13 amp three-pin fittings (plugs and sockets) should be three-core cables with an earth (protective) conductor.  This conductor should always be terminated in accordance with the manufacturer's instructions.  Extension cables should not be excessively long as the use of such cables may result in a failure to operate the electrical protection in the event of an equipment fault, due to the high electrical impedances of the system.  Drum-type extension cables should be unwound before use to avoid a fire risk (a fire risk occurs if high currents pass through a coiled cable).

60  All portable and transportable electrical equipment, flexible cables, plugs, sockets, connectors and extension leads should be separately identified and regularly visually inspected for damage and be routinely electrically tested to ensure continued electrical integrity.  Any equipment etc which is found damaged during visual inspection or fails an electrical test should be withdrawn from service immediately for repair/ replacement.  Guidance on inspection, testing and maintenance of portable equipment may be found in the HSE Guidance Note *The safe use of portable electrical apparatus* (see Appendix 5). Appropriate records of inspection and testing should be kept. The intervals between inspections and tests for equipment need to be established by the employer and should take account of the use and possible abuse of the equipment concerned, for example floor cleaning machinery every three months.  Typical routine electrical checks for portable apparatus are set out in Appendix 2.

## STEAM AND WATER PRESSURE CLEANERS

61  A typical steam/water pressure cleaner consists of a trolley-mounted oil fired boiler, water tank with ball valve, detergent tank, a pump driven by an electric motor, a starter and a length of reinforced hose terminating in a lance.  There is usually a flexible cable for the electricity supply and a hose for the water supply.  Other machines do not have a boiler and detergent tank and clean by high pressure water jet.  They are commonly used in warehouses for cleaning plant and vehicles.

The use of these machines generally creates wet environments and the operator's clothing, skin and footwear usually become wet and very conductive. In such circumstances fatal electric shocks can occur if the lance becomes 'live' due to an electric fault while the operator is holding it, for example the earth conductor can be pulled from its plug terminal and touch the phase terminal making the metalwork live.  The lance is connected to the metalwork via the wire reinforcement of the hose and the water or liquid inside it.  The operator holding the lance completes the circuit to earth via his or her wet body and feet.

62  The following general precautions should be adopted:

(a)  use a 110 volt supply derived from a transformer with the mid-point of the secondary winding earthed if single phase, or the star point of 3 phase, giving 55 volts or 64 volts phase to earth, respectively;

(b)  use a circulating current earth monitoring device. This works by continuously proving the integrity of the earth continuity conductor between the device and the equipment. A break in this circuit operates a trip device of a circuit breaker and interrupts the electric supply to the equipment;

(c)  where earth monitoring is not provided a residual current device (RCD) of the current operated type should be used to control the supply to the equipment. (These units are also known as earth leakage circuit breakers, ELCBs.) They work by detecting earth leakage currents and interrupt the supply circuit if the leakage rises above a rated tripping current. Any RCD used to provide this additional protection should have a rated tripping current not exceeding 30 mA. The device should not have any time-delay feature, it must be a device complying with either BS 4293 or BS 7071. Such devices will operate in a time not exceeding 40 ms when a fault current of 150 mA flows, the time of operation when a fault current of the rated tripping value flows should not exceed 240 ms. (These devices are commonly referred to as 30 mA/30 m devices).  For small single phase machines (up to 3 kW) plug-in RCD units may be used but care should be taken that they are located where they will not be splashed, or put in a suitable enclosure. For larger machines, RCDs built into purpose-made enclosures with socket outlets and isolating switches or fused switches may be installed between the flexible cable to the machine and the supply. An RCD fitted in the supply to a transformer will not provide any protection on the secondary side of the transformer.

Any RCD fitted should be provided with a test button. This test button should be operated each time before use. If the RCD fails to trip, the system should not be used. A competent electrician should be called to rectify the fault.

RCDs are not a substitute for good installation practice; they are an additional form of protection. To ensure adequate earth fault paths, structural and other metalwork should be bonded to each other and to earth in areas where steam and water pressure cleaners are used. Advice on earthing and bonding may be found in the IEE Wiring Regulations and in BS Code of Practice 1013. All earthing and bonding should be installed and connected by a competent electrician.

(Both circulating current earth monitoring and RCD protection systems can fail-to-danger. Units which incorporate both RCD protection and earth-monitoring systems may reduce the effect of failure of an individual device by providing a degree of redundancy);

(d) plugs and sockets should conform to BS 4343 or BS 196. Domestic pattern BS 1363 or BS 546 plugs should not be used;

(e) plugs and sockets situated near the work site or outdoors should be at least to IP 55 (BS 5490) to provide adequate protection against ingress of water etc;

(f) cable entries should be effectively sealed and rubber shrouds should be provided over cable glands. BS 4343 drip-proof (IPX2) plugs and sockets are suitable for use indoors away from the water spray area;

(g) flexible cables to these machines may need to be further protected by means of flexible braided armour, provided as screens (see HSE Guidance Note *Elecrical hazards from steam/water pressure cleaners etc* - see Appendix 5). Where braided armoured/screened flexible cables are used, the terminations into connectors, plugs etc must be suitable and appropriate to terminate the screen/armour and earth it;

(h) waterproof protective clothing and eye protectors should be provided for use by operators.

## SUBSTANCES HAZARDOUS TO HEALTH

63  The Control of Substances Hazardous to Health Regulations 1988 (COSHH) and the associated Approved Codes of Practice lay down essential requirements and a framework for controlling the exposure of people to hazardous substances arising from work activities. A principal requirement of COSHH is that an assessment should be made of the health risks created by work activities and the steps that need to be taken to prevent or, where this is not reasonably practicable, adequately control exposure of people to these substances.

64  Substances that are 'hazardous to health' include substances that are required to be labelled 'very toxic', 'toxic', 'corrosive', 'harmful' or 'irritant' (see Appendix 3) and substances which have maximum exposure limits or occupational exposure standards set by the Health and Safety Executive.  They also include harmful micro-organisms, substantial quantities of dust and any material, mixture or compound used at work or arising from work activities which can harm a person's health.

65  The COSHH Regulations do not apply to activities where the Control of Asbestos at Work Regulations or the Control of Lead at Work Regulations apply, or where the risk is solely from radiation, explosion, flammability, pressure or temperature.

66  Many hazardous substances are likely to be found in warehouses, for example adhesives, solvents, corrosives, acids, gases, powders, dusts and general and specific chemicals. People may be exposed to such substances in use in warehouses, for example using solvents to clean parts of a lift truck or other equipment.  Other circumstances in warehouses which may give rise to a risk of exposure to these substances would include:

(a)  leaks from packages and containers;

(b)  accidental spillage;

(c)  puncture of packages or containers, for example by the forks of a lift truck;

(d)  subdividing substances or breaking down from bulk storage;

(e)  generating hazardous substances on site, for example exhaust fumes and accidental mixing of incompatible products during storage.

67  The Regulations require all employers to:

(a)  assess the risk to health arising from work and the precautions that are needed;

(b)  introduce appropriate control measures to prevent or adequately control exposure to hazardous substances;

(c)  ensure that control measures are used and that equipment is  properly maintained and procedures observed;

(d)  where necessary, monitor the exposure of workers and, if appropriate, provide or carry out health surveillance; and

(e)  inform, instruct and train employees about risks and what  precautions to take.

### Assessment

68  To tackle any problem, first assess what the problem is and its extent before deciding what, if anything, you need to do about it. The assessment should be a systematic review of all work undertaken which asks:

(a)  what substances are present and in what form?

(b)  what harmful effects are possible and how would they affect the body? For example, inhalation risks from dusts or vapours, skin contact/absorption from solvents, ingestion of chemicals from  skin contamination;

(c)  where and how are substances actually used or handled?

(d)  what harmful substances are given off or produced?

(e)  who could be affected, to what extent and for how long?

(f)  under what circumstances would people be affected?

(g)  how likely is it that exposure will happen?

(h)  what precautions need to be taken to comply with the rest of the COSHH Regulations?

69  All these questions should be considered and related to what actually happens in the workplace. In this way assessment conclusions will reflect only what is relevant to the real risk in the particular

circumstance. In all but the simplest cases the assessment will need to be written down. Much of the information concerning the hazardous nature of substances should be provided by the supplier who has a legal duty to make adequate information available. Each work activity or situation that may give rise to a foreseeable risk to health must be formally assessed. Much assessment will be within the scope of company staff who should use common sense in following the principles set out. Complex assessments may require the services of a competent occupational hygienist.

70 Sufficient information will need to be recorded to show why decisions about risks and precautions have been made. The assessment should be kept at the warehouse to which it relates.

71 In some cases the quantities, the exposure time or the effects may be such that the substances do not or could not constitute a risk and therefore no further action under COSHH would be necessary. If this is the case the employer must have adequate information to verify this conclusion.

### Prevention of exposure

72 The employer is required to ensure that exposure of people to hazardous substances is prevented or, if this is not reasonably practicable, adequately controlled. The first aim should be to prevent exposure by:

(a) changing the system, for example use ready supplied pre-packaged substances instead of breaking down from bulk;

(b) substituting a hazardous substance with a safe or safer substance or using it in a safer form, for example use pelletised material instead of a powdered product.

### Control of exposure

73 When this is not reasonably practicable the employer must ensure adequate control of exposure by, for example:

(a) totally enclosing the process;

(b) partial enclosure and extract equipment;

(c) general ventilation;

(d) safe systems of work and handling procedures;

(e) personal protective equipment (PPE), for example respirators, eye protectors, protective clothing. Note: PPE is NOT an alternative to other means of control and must only be considered when adequate control is not reasonably practicable by other means.

### Using the controls

74 Employers must ensure that the control measures are properly used or applied. Employees must make full and proper use of the controls and report any defects to their employer.

### Maintenance of controls

75 Employers have a duty to ensure that the control measures are kept in efficient working order and good repair. If the control measures consist of engineering controls they should be examined and tested at regular intervals. In particular, local exhaust ventilation equipment should be tested at least once every 14 months and a simple record kept of the results. Records of examinations and tests must be kept for five years.

### Planning for emergencies

76 If it is reasonably foreseeable that leaks, spills or other uncontrolled releases of a hazardous substance could occur, the employer must consider ways of limiting the extent of the risks and of regaining control as quickly as possible. Such ways include having:

(a) people and equipment available to minimise and control quantities released;

(b) defined emergency procedures and appropriate training (including evacuation procedures where necessary);

(c) safe methods for disposal and decontamination;

(d) sufficient and suitable personal protective equipment;

(e) suitable means for decontamination of people and equipment.

### Informing employees

77 Employees have to be informed, instructed and trained so that they know and understand:

(a) the risks arising from their work;

(b) the precautions to be taken.

78 An employer's obligation under COSHH does not finish with the assessment. This is merely the first stage. After the assessment has been carried out controls have to be implemented, employees informed and, finally, the whole situation should be kept under review to ensure not only that the control measures are being carried out, but also to check whether there have been any significant

changes to working practices or substances used which would merit reassessment.

Practical guidance on COSHH is given in some detail in the associated Approved Codes of Practice (see Appendix 5 for details).

### Asbestos and lead

79  COSHH does not apply to these substances as they are each subject to specific Regulations.

#### Asbestos

80  Asbestos-containing materials are not likely to be used or handled in warehouse premises. Asbestos-containing materials may, however, be present in a warehouse, for example, boiler and pipework lagging.  Those materials could release asbestos fibres if in a poor condition or damaged, for example by lift truck.

81  If suspicious materials are discovered it is essential to seek specialist advice to determine whether or not they contain asbestos.  Advice on the identification, assessment and management of existing asbestos in buildings is in a Department of the Environment publication *Asbestos materials in buildings* (see Appendix 5).

82  Work with asbestos insulation and/or coating should, with minor exceptions, be carried out only by a contractor holding a current licence issued by HSE under the Asbestos (Licensing) Regulations 1983.  All work with asbestos, including minor repair and maintenance work, is subject to the Control of Asbestos at Work Regulations (CAWR) 1987 and should be carried out in accordance with those Regulations and the associated Approved Codes of Practice (see Appendix 5).  In particular, CAWR requires that an assessment should be made of the health risks created by work with asbestos, and the steps that need to be taken to prevent or, when this is not reasonably practicable, adequately control exposure to asbestos.

#### Lead

83  Compounds of lead may be stored or handled in such a way, for example breaking down from bulk, as to be subject to the Control of Lead at Work Regulations 1980 and the associated Approved Code of Practice (see Appendix 5).  In such circumstances, working conditions should be assessed to determine whether exposure is significant and if further action is necessary to control the risk of exposure to lead. If in doubt seek specialist advice.

## NOISE

### General

84  Sources of noise in warehouses include lift trucks, compressors and conveyor systems.  Such sources may give rise to potentially hazardous levels of noise which can cause incurable hearing damage. Noise at work can cause other problems such as disturbance, interference with communication and stress.

### The Noise at Work Regulations 1989

85  The Noise at Work Regulations place an obligation on all employers to reduce the risk of damage to the hearing of their employees from exposure to noise to the lowest level reasonably practicable.

### Action levels

86  There are three action levels of noise defined in the Regulations:

(a)  First Action Level - a daily personal noise exposure (LEP,d) of 85 dB(A).

(b)  Second Action Level - a daily personal noise exposure (LEP,d) of 90 dB(A).

(c)  Peak Action Level - a peak sound pressure of 200 Pascals (140 dB).

87  As a rough guide the First Action Level is likely to be reached when people speaking normally have difficulty in being heard clearly by someone who is about two metres away. The Regulations require the employer to take certain basic steps where an employee is likely to be exposed to noise at or above the First Action Level.  These steps together with additional action must also be taken where an employee is likely to be exposed at or above the Second or Peak Action Level.

### Assessment

88  Employers are required to arrange for a noise assessment whenever an employee is likely to be exposed at or above the First or Peak Action Level. The assessment will need to:

(a)  identify all workers likely to be so exposed and;

(b)  provide the employer with the information required to decide what kind of action needs to be taken.  For example the assessment should tell the employer:

    (i)  the nature of the problem (if any) and how serious it is;

    (ii)  who is at risk;

(iii) where the risk exists;

(iv) very broadly why the problem exists, for example noisy lift trucks and the air compressor.

89 A suitable record of the assessment must be kept. Such a record must include details of:

(a) the workplaces, areas or jobs assessed and what the results were;

(b) when the assessment was made.

90 The task of carrying out a noise assessment must be done by a competent person, ie someone who is capable of not only measuring noise but of bringing together and presenting enough information about noise exposure to enable the employer to make correct decisions on what should be done to comply with the Regulations.

### Reduction of noise exposure

91 Where employees are exposed at or above the Second or Peak Action Levels the employer must reduce exposure as far as is reasonably practicable by means other than provision of personal ear protectors. In some cases noise can be obviated by more fundamental changes, such as using a different, quieter process, or devising alternative ways of doing the job. Where this is not reasonably practicable, the employer will need to implement a programme of control measures. Programmes to control noise by engineering means will only be effective if the staff working on them are competent in noise control engineering, or advised by someone who is.

92 Limiting the time spent in noisy areas, for example by providing a noise refuge, can also help to restrict daily personal exposure but usually only to a limited extent, for example halving the exposure time will reduce LEP,d by only 3 dB(A). If this method is to be relied upon the exposure time will need to be effectively controlled.

### Ear protection

93 The duty to provide ear protectors depends on the exposure level:

(a) between First and Second Action Levels the employer is required to provide ear protectors to employees who ask for them;

(b) above Second and Peak Action Levels the employer is required to provide ear protectors to all workers likely to be so exposed.

94 Detailed advice on the types of protector and their selection is given in *Noise Guide No 5* (see Appendix 5).

95 In areas where the noise level is potentially hazardous and the employees are provided with, and use, hearing protectors, the employer still has to reduce the noise levels in the working area and keep to a minimum the time workers spend there, so far as is reasonably practicable.

96 An Ear Protection Zone means any part of the premises where any employee is likely to be exposed to the Second Action Level or above or to the Peak Action Level or above. Wherever reasonably practicable the employer will have to designate Ear Protection Zones and display signs showing that they are areas where ear protectors are required to be worn (see Figure 3).

**Figure 3** Sign for informing that ear protectors must be worn (white on a circular blue background)

### Ear protection zones

97 A cold store compressor room is one example of an area likely to be designated as an ear protection zone. The employer must ensure so far as is reasonably practicable that all who go into these zones wear protectors. Where it is not reasonably practicable to mark ear protection zones, for example where noise sources are moved about a great deal, adequate alternative arrangements should be made to help make sure that employees know where ear protectors should be worn.

### Information, instruction and training

98 Where employees are likely to be exposed at or above any of the action levels, the employer is required to provide each employee with adequate information, instruction and training. Information should include:

(a) the likely noise exposure and consequent risk to hearing;

(b) how to report defects in ear protectors and noise control equipment;

(c) where and how ear protectors can be obtained;

(d) the employee's duties under the Regulations;

(e) the advisability of seeking medical advice if an employee thinks there is something wrong with his or her hearing.

**Table 4**  Requirements of the Noise at Work Regulations

| Action required where $L_{EP,d}$ is likely to be: | below 85 dB(A) | 85 dB(A) First AL | 90 dB(A) Second AL |
|---|---|---|---|
| **EMPLOYER'S DUTIES** | | | 2 |
| **General duty to reduce risk** | | | |
| Risk of hearing damage to be reduced to the lowest level reasonably practicable (Reg 6) | • | • | • |
| **Assessment of noise exposure** | | | |
| Noise assessments to be made by a competent person (Reg 4) | | • | • |
| Record of assessments to be kept until a new one is made (Reg 5) | | • | • |
| **Noise reduction** | | | |
| Reduce exposure to noise as far as is reasonably practicable by means other than ear protectors (Reg 7) | | | • |
| **Provision of information to workers** | | | |
| Provide adequate information, instruction and training about risks to hearing, what employees should do to minimise risk, how they can obtain ear protectors if they are exposed between 85 and 90 dB(A), and their obligations under the Regulations (Reg 11) | | • | • |
| Mark ear protection zones with notices, so far as is reasonably practicable (Reg 9) | | | • |
| **Ear protectors** | | | |
| Ensure so far as is practicable that protectors are:<br>- provided to employees who ask for them (Reg 8(1));<br>- provided to all exposed (Reg 8(2));<br>- maintained and repaired (Reg 10(1)(b));<br>- used by all exposed (Reg 10(1)(a)). | | •<br><br>• | <br>•<br>•<br>• |
| Ensure so far as reasonably practicable that all who go into a marked ear protection zone use ear protectors (Reg 9(1)(b)) | | | •<br><br>3 |
| **Maintenance and use of equipment** | | | |
| Ensure so far as is reasonable that:<br>- all equipment provided under the Regulations is used, except for the ear protectors provided between 85 and 90 dB(A) (Reg 10(1)(a));<br>- ensure all equipment is maintained (Reg 10(1)(b)). | | •<br>• | •<br>• |
| **EMPLOYEE'S DUTIES** | | | |
| **Use of equipment** | | | |
| So far as is practicable:<br>- use ear protectors (Reg 10(2));<br>- use any other protective equipment (Reg 10(2));<br>- report any defects discovered to his or her employer (Reg 10(2)). | | •<br>• | •<br>• |
| **MACHINE MAKER'S AND SUPPLIER'S DUTIES** | | | |
| **Provision of information** | | | |
| Provide information on the noise likely to be generated (Reg 12) | | • | • |

Notes:
1  The dB(A) action levels are values of daily personal exposure to noise $L_{EP,d}$).
2  All the actions indicated at 90 dB(A) are also required where the peak sound pressure is at or above 200 Pa (140 dB).
3  This requirement applies to all who enter the zones, even if they do not stay long enough to receive an exposure of 90 dB(A) $L_{EP,d}$.

Instruction and training will include what the employee should do to minimise the risk, such as the proper way to use ear protectors and other equipment, how to look after it, and where ear protectors should be used.

### Employees' duties

99  Employees' duties include:

(a)  co-operating with the assessment of noise exposure;

(b)  using noise control measures in accordance with the employer's instructions;

(c)  wearing the ear protectors provided;

(d)  taking care of ear protectors and noise control equipment;

(e)  reporting any defect found in ear protectors or other protective measures.

### Practical considerations

100  Before purchasing potentially noisy equipment, for example compressors, ask for noise information from the manufacturer or supplier so that a positive choice can be made. Noise emissions can be predicted and noise control can be planned for. Proper maintenance of equipment will help to reduce noise levels. Careful consideration needs to be given to ensure that audible warnings, for example on lift trucks, can be heard if workers need to wear ear protectors.

### Summary

101  The main requirements of the Noise at Work Regulations are summarised in Table 4.

## WORK-RELATED UPPER LIMB DISORDERS

102  Work-related upper limb disorders can be caused, aggravated or precipitated by forceful repetitive or sustained static activities, particularly in combination with awkward postures, occurring over a period of time with insufficient time being allowed for recovery. The term upper limb disorders covers a range of different conditions affecting the soft tissues of the hand, wrist, arm and shoulder. Work-related upper limb disorders may occur in the warehouse setting, for example, in workers involved in order picking, packing or keyboard operations.

103  Musculoskeletal problems in the upper limbs are common in the general population but links between some work activities and these conditions have long been recognised. Reliable statistics on the incidence and prevalence of work-related upper limb disorders are not available, but it is thought

that they account for a considerable amount of occupational ill health. Conditions that are included under the umbrella of work-related upper limb disorders are tenosynovitis, carpal tunnel syndrome, peritendonitis crepitans, tennis elbow/golfer's elbow.

### Prevention or control of risk

104 Where a particular job is suspected of causing a work-related upper limb disorder some form of risk assessment should be made with the aim of identifying specific risk factors. An ergonomics check-list such as is printed in the HSE's publication *Work-related upper limb disorders: a guide to prevention* (see Appendix 5) can be used. Information contained in Appendix 2 will be a useful tool for assessing risk factors.

105 Where a new job or task is being introduced the ergonomic factors involved should be assessed, so as to avoid or eliminate any risk of operators developing upper limb disorders. A combination of different approaches to eliminate or prevent work-related upper limb disorders will be required. Some will be based on work design, others on organisational arrangements. Work design solutions should aim to reduce force levels involved in a task, for example by using jigs or clamps instead of the hands to grip parts; minimise repetitive movements, for example by restructuring the job so that the worker has a larger and more varied number of tasks to perform; eliminate postural problems that may be caused by poor workstation and equipment design.
Consideration should be given to the possible use of mechanisation or automation to reduce or eliminate the risks of developing work-related upper limb disorders.

106 Organisational arrangements should include selection of personnel, to fit the worker to the task; provision of training and instruction; job rotation and adequate rest periods. Special consideration should be given to new employees who should be introduced at a slower work rate, followed by gradual upgrading to the roles of the experienced workforce.

### Check-list for employers

● Have you looked at tasks to determine whether they might be responsible for causing work-related upper limb disorders?

● Can mechanised or automatic systems of work be introduced?

● Can job rotation be introduced?

● Can job enlargement or restructuring be of benefit?

● Will redesign of the workstation or tools eliminate postural problems?

● Would reduction of machine pace reduce or eliminate the problem?

● Are tools well maintained, for example are cutting edges kept sharp so as to reduce force required?

● Has adequate training and instruction been given to employees and is the effectiveness of the training etc being monitored?
For further details and information on minimising work-related upper limb disorders see Manual Handling section.

107 In general, the method of storage depends on the shape and fragility of the article. Long thin articles are generally stored in some form of horizontal racking and box-shaped articles or loose materials in sacks built into a stack, with suitable bonding to ensure stability (see Figure 4).

**Figure 4** Pallet load, showing bonding

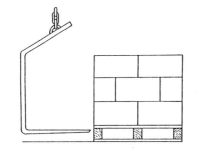

**Figure 5** 'C' hook pallet fork attachments can improve handling of pallets by cranes

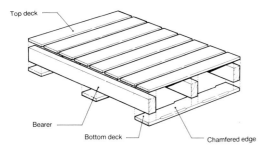

108 Cylindrical articles can be stored on their sides or on end. When such articles are stored on their sides the floor level tier should be properly secured to prevent movement. Subsequent tiers can rest on the preceding one or be laid on battens and wedged.

109 Storage areas should be specifically designated and clearly marked. The layout of the storage and handling areas should be carefully considered to avoid tight corners, awkwardly placed doors, pillars, uneven surfaces and changes of gradient. The use of guardrails to protect pedestrian routes should be considered.

110 Where materials are handled by crane or lift truck they should be placed on suitable battens or other suitable material, so that a sling or the forks can be inserted. Pallets handled by crane should only be lifted by attachments suitable for that pallet design. A suitable 'C' hook pallet attachment should be used where appropriate (see Figure 5). Where fork lift trucks are used it is possible for most materials to be palletised and stacked as complete pallet loads, or on pallet racking.

## PALLETS

111 A pallet is a portable platform, with or without superstructure, for the assembly of a quantity of goods to form a unit load for handling and storage by mechanical means. They are widely used for the storage and transit of goods.

**Figure 6** Flat pallet

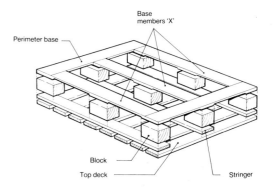

(a) Two-way entry non-reversible(topside view)
A pallet whose bearers permit the entry of forks from two opposite directions only.

(b) Four-way entry (underside view) A pallet whose blocks permit the entry of forks from all four directions. Some pallets are designed without base members 'X'.

Notes:

1 A reversible pallet is a pallet with similar top and bottom decks, either of which would take the same load. They are not suitable for use with pallet trucks as the small wheels on the fingers will cause damage and separation of the bottom deck.

2 A wing pallet is a flat pallet whose deck (or decks) project beyond the outer bearers to facilitate the use of lifting slings. They are not suitable for drive-in or drive-through racking where the dimension between beam rails of the racking has to match the overall width of the pallet, as the wings are not strong enough to support substantial loads.

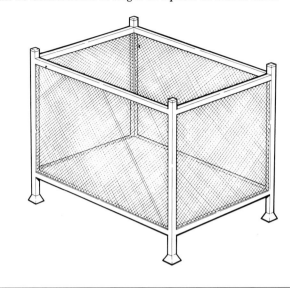

**Figure 7** Box pallet. A pallet with or without a lid, having a superstructure of at least three fixed, removable or collapsible vertical sides, solid, slatted or mesh, which permit stacking. Can be constructed of angle or square or round tube.

112 Flat pallets, post pallets and box pallets are the most common types of pallets used in warehouses (see Figures 6-8.) A cage pallet is a special design of pallet having a superstructure of four attached, collapsible vertical sides usually slotted or mesh. Such pallets are designed to permit stacking by mechanical means. It is used both for transit of goods and as a display and selection unit for merchandising in retail outlets, ie goods can be put on sale without further unpacking and handling. Stillages are box pallets, post pallets, and cage pallets which are not stackable (see BS 3810: Part 1). This term may however be used 'loosely' to describe these types of pallet even when they are stackable. Pallets can be constructed of a number of materials such as steel, plastic or timber. Flat pallets are usually constructed of timber. Pallets should be of sound construction, sound material and of adequate strength. It is recommended that pallet design should satisfy the requirements of BS 2629, Part 3. World-wide the design and dimensions of pallets vary.

113 If pallet racking (see Figure 6) is used in the warehouse the type is of key importance when considering which type of pallet to use. Consideration must be given to the bending stresses exerted on timber flat pallets from this type of storage.

### Use of flat pallets

114 Flat timber pallets form an essential part of many mechanical handling systems in warehouses. Accidents directly attributable to these pallets usually arise from six main sources:

(a) poor design;

(b) poor construction;

(c) the use of a pallet which is unsuitable for a particular load;

(d) the continued use of a damaged pallet;

(e) bad handling;

(f) the use of a pallet which is unsuitable for a particular racking system.

115 The majority of pallets are designed for the carriage of a particular class or type of goods and to be handled or stored by a particular method, for example a pallet intended for the carriage of boxed cereals, handled by a lift truck and stored singly in racking, will not usually be suitable for goods such as cans of paint, lifting by bar sling or stacking four high. It should also be noted that a pallet designed specifically to carry evenly distributed loads, such as boxed cereals, may not be strong enough to carry concentrated loads, such as an electric motor of the same weight.

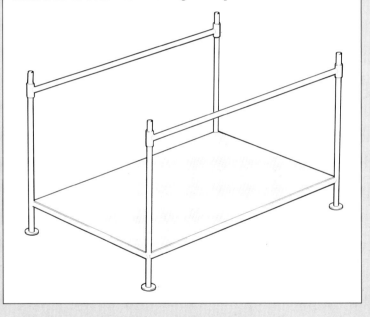

**Figure 8** Post pallet. A pallet having a fixed or detachable superstructure of posts to permit stacking, with or without rails. Can be constructed of angle or square or rounded tube.

116 Where mixed racking systems are installed, the use of pallets which require a different orientation for each racking system, for example a four-way entry pallet without base members 'X' - see Figure 6(b), would not be regarded as suitable. A pallet design which is suitable for all the racking systems regardless of orientation should be used.

### Loading of pallets

117 Pallets should be loaded to an established pattern designed to achieve maximum stability and safety within the rated load. Loads should be applied gradually and unless the pallet has been specifically designed for point loading should, as far as possible, be uniformly distributed over the deck area. As a general guide, the height of the

**Figure 9** Common pallet handling faults which can damage deck boards

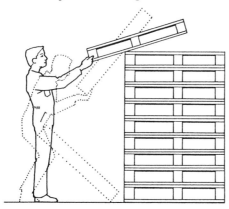

Any sliding and dropping action
should be avoided

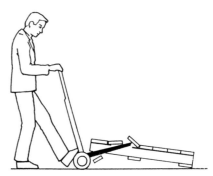

Improving manhandling - with for
example misuse of a sack truck - can
loosen boards

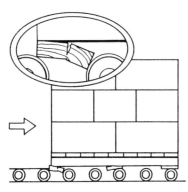

The spacing of pallet conveyor rollers
should be less than that of pallet base
members otherwise jamming can occur

... 'ramps and bumpy floors can cause
loads to be jolted and bases of pallets
to be grazed'

load should not exceed the longest base dimension of the pallet. Shrink or stretch wrapping the load usually provides greater security, minimising the possibility of movements of goods, and it may be possible in certain circumstances to safely transport loads taller than the largest base dimension of the pallet, for example palletised loads approximately to the internal height of closed vehicles. This should only be done, however, where the employer has carefully assessed the stability of the load components, the load configuration and any special features such as wrapping, strapping etc.

### Stacking palletised loads (block stacking)

118 Stacking of palletised loads of cartons and packs which are capable of being crushed should be avoided as the strength and stability of the load cannot be maintained. Loads which are capable of being stacked directly on top of each other should be positioned on a firm level base. It may be necessary to provide additional packing on top of the lower palletised load depending on the characteristics of the load and design of the pallet. Generally, such stacks should not be more than four loads high. In some circumstances, dependent on the height, strength and stability of the loads, taller stacks may be built. The maximum permissible height may be up to six loads high provided that the pallet itself and the packaging of

the stored goods is designed to exceed the four-high strength. Adequate clearance should be maintained between rows to ensure safe stacking and withdrawal. Stacks should be checked periodically for stability and corrective measures taken where necessary.

### Safe pallet use

119 The following points should be considered:

(a) an effective pallet damage inspection and out-sorting routine should be established. Further information on pallet inspection criteria can be found in the HSE Guidance Note *Safety in the use of timber pallets* (see Appendix 5);

(b) all pallets should be inspected each time before use, to ensure that they are in a safe condition. Damaged pallets should be withdrawn for repair or destruction. The repair of a pallet should restore it to its original design specification;

(c) empty pallets should be carefully handled and not dragged or thrown about. They should not be handled by methods likely to loosen deckboards, for example wedging the platform of a sack barrow between top and bottom deck boards (see Figure 9);

(d) if pallet trucks are used, care should be taken to ensure that the small finger wheels (also

**Figure 10** Pallet truck fingers of unsuitable length can cause baseboard damage and be dangerous to personnel

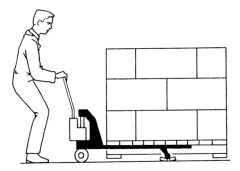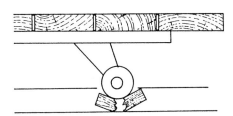

**Figure 11** Load packaging

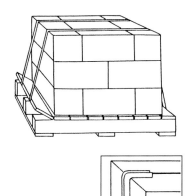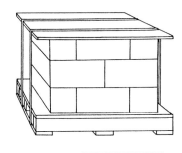

ANGLE IRON

EDGE PROTECTOR

(a) Tight strapping of too small loads can distort deckboards.

(b) Dunnage and other methods can improve load packaging.

**Figure 12** Correct procedure for entering a pallet

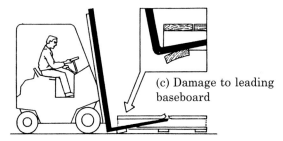

(c) Damage to leading baseboard

(a) Mast should be absolutely vertical

(b) Mast should not be tilted backwards until forks have fully entered and lifted the pallet.

**Figure 13** Optimum distance between forks should be known in relation to pallet size

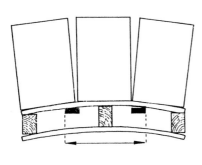

**Figure 14** Turntable pallet stretch wrap machine

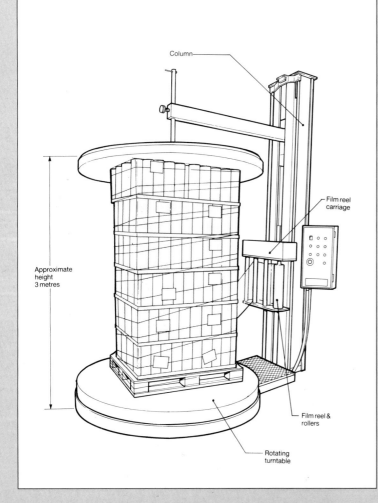

Column

Film reel carriage

Approximate height 3 metres

Film reel & rollers

Rotating turntable

(f) care should be exercised when using strapping to secure loads to pallets, as deck boards can be pulled from the bearers (see Figure 11);

(g) to avoid damage to pallets and in order to lift palletised loads safely, the forks of a handling device should extend into the pallet to least at 3/4 of its depth.

Note: The forks should not extend beyond the pallet as protruding forks could:

(i) make contact with or lift an adjacent load(s) causing it to overturn or collapse; or

(ii) find their way underneath a fixed structure, for example racking, during lifting causing overloading of the truck and/or serious damage to the structure.

120 Only authorised, trained and competent personnel should operate lift trucks (see paragraphs 166-171). Users should comply with the HSC Approved Code of Practice *Rider operated lift trucks - operator training* (see Appendix 5).

121 Operators should receive instruction on the correct method of handling pallets, which must emphasise that:

(a) the mast should be in the vertical position when entering and leaving the pallet (see Figure 12);

(b) the pallet should be housed against the heel of the forks;

(c) the forks should enter the pallet squarely;

(d) the forks should be correctly spaced for the pallet load being lifted (see Figure 13);

(e) pallets should not be pulled or pushed along the ground;

(f) loads should be carefully and gently placed on the stack below;

(g) pallets should be lowered onto racking beams and never slid across the top surface of such beams.

## TURNTABLE PALLET STRETCH WRAP MACHINES (see Figure 14)

122 These machines are commonly used in warehouse premises to wrap a pallet load in a sheet of plastic film to provide stability, weatherproofing and protection to the load during storage or distribution. The pallet load is usually placed on to the turntable of the machine using a lift truck or pallet truck, the plastic film is then attached to the pallet load manually, for example by tying to the pallet, and wrapping is carried out by rotating the load on the turntable while the film reel is carried

known as trail or guide wheels) do not damage the base boards (see Figure 10). Chamfered edges to the bottom deck boards will assist entry of the pallet truck fork arms;

(e) expendable pallets, ie pallets designed for one delivery only, should be clearly marked to this effect. They should not be re-used;

vertically up and down on a column. Some machines are fitted with a top clamp which descends to steady the pallet load while the wrapping cycle is carried out.

123 Common hazards associated with the use of turntable pallet stretch wrap machines include:

(a) trapping of a person's body between the moving pallet load and fixed structures;

(b) trapping of a person's body between the moving pallet load and fixed parts of the machine;

(c) trapping of a hand by moving parts, for example drive mechanisms, chains, sprockets;

(d) trapping of a foot between the power driven turntable and its surround;

(e) trapping of a foot between the underside of the film reel carriage and floor or framework of the machine;

(f) trapping of a hand/arm between the top clamp and load.

124 The following safeguards should be adopted when turntable pallet stretch wrap machines are used:

(a) users should ensure that the area around the turntable to a minimum distance of 500 mm (1 m is recommended) from the turntable edge is level and marked with fluorescent orange-red or safety colour yellow and black lines (see BS 5378). This area should be clear of obstructions to allow safe access for trucks to load and unload (see Figure 12). Suitable systems of work should be adopted to avoid the danger of overhang for example, by ensuring correct positioning of the pallet and ensuring that the pallet is of the appropriate size;

(b) there should be a minimum horizontal clearance of 500 mm between the turntable edge and any fixed parts of the machine or film reel carriage;

(c) the drive mechanism to the turntable should be completely encased;

(d) suitable fixed guards should be provided for chains and sprockets in the film reel carriage column. Guarding may not be necessary where the film reel carriage is moved by means of a collar driven by a protected lead screw (see BS 5304:1988 *Safety of machinery* - see Appendix 5);

(e) the turntable should be circular to minimise the risk of foot trapping. Any gap between the turntable and its surround should not exceed 5 mm;

(f) to prevent trapping a foot between the underside of the film reel carriage and the floor or other fixed framework of the machine, a clearance of at least 100 mm should be maintained. Where this is not possible a suitable trip device which will stop the motion of the film reel carriage, should be provided. The film reel carriage should not restart automatically if stopped by a trip device; positive restart action, for example the operation of a 'start' button should be necessary after the obstruction is removed. Similar protection is required between the film feed carriage and the top clamp support at the other end of the carriage travel, unless safe by position;

(g) to prevent entrapment between the top clamp and load, the underside of the clamp should be covered with suitable resilient material at least 25 mm thick. This should be renewed if its resilience deteriorates. The top clamp pressure should be limited to prevent or reduce the risk of injury if a person's arm comes between the top of the pallet load and underside of the top clamp;

(h) to allow for uneven loading, the diagonal measurement of the largest pallet load should be at least 100 mm less than the diameter of the turntable, for example for a standard 1200 mm by 1000 mm pallet the turntable size should be 1650 mm diameter;

(i) controls and switches should be grouped and mounted in one panel, clearly marked to indicate their function and mode of operation, and situated to allow the operative to occupy a safe position with full view of the load;

(j) easily accessible emergency stop buttons should be provided and be of the palm or mushroom type, coloured red. Once operated, the stop buttons should remain in operation until reset;

(k) as an alternative to safeguarding the hazards individually, the turntable column and film reel should be provided with an interlocked enclosure in accordance with BS 5304 (see Appendix 5).

125 In some specialised warehousing situations pallet wrappers or strappers which are conveyor-fed and operate automatically (including those where the pallet remains stationary while the reel passes round it on a rotating arm) may be found. Such machines generally require a higher standard of guarding and as a minimum should be provided with interlocked enclosures to BS 5304. Further advice on the principles of safeguarding relevant to these machines may be found in the HSE publication *Industrial robot safety* (see Appendix 5).

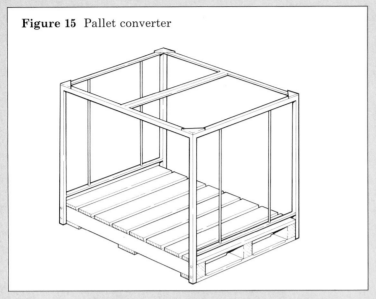

**Figure 15** Pallet converter

## PALLET INVERTERS

126 These mechanically operated machines are designed so that a defective pallet at the bottom of a palletised load can be easily removed and replaced with a sound pallet without the need to de-stack the load by hand. They may also be used to change from one type of pallet to another. Pallet inverters should only be used where a pallet carries non-crushable materials stacked in a manner that allows inversion. The basic operation is as follows:

1   Palletised load with defective pallet placed on to the platform of the machine by lift truck or pallet truck.

2   Load clamped between platform and top plate.

3   Load inverted by machine.

4   Clamping mechanism released.

5   Pallet removed and replaced with sound or different type of pallet (by hand).

6   Palletised load re-clamped.

7   Load re-inverted.

8   Platform descends with palletised load to original position.

127 The existing hazards at pallet inverters are known to be:

(a)  the trapping points between the dangerous moving parts of the pallet inverter;

(b)  the trapping points between the moving parts of the pallet inverter and its fixed structure;

(c)  the trapping points between moving parts of the pallet inverter and the fixed structure of the building or structures surrounding the pallet inverter;

(d)  the trapping points between the moving platform and the palletised load;

(e)  the trapping points between the moving platform and the ground or loading bay during descent.

128 The assessment of the risks associated with the use of pallet inverters should lead to adoption of the following precautions:

(a)  locate the pallet inverter in a suitable part of the warehouse where non-essential employees can be excluded from its area of operation;

(b)  provide interlocked enclosure guards. Further advice on interlocked guards and other safety devices is contained in BS 5304:1988 *Safety of machinery* (see Appendix 5). The enclosure guards should be so designed, installed and adjusted that:

(i)   until the guard is closed the interlock prevents the machinery from operating by interrupting the power;

(ii)  either the guard remains locked closed until the risk of injury from the hazard has passed, or opening the guard causes the hazard to be eliminated before access is possible (ie the machine comes to rest before access is possible);

(c)  Operators should be trained and instructed and be competent in the correct method of use of the machine and made aware of the potential dangers.

## PALLET CONVERTERS (See Figure 15)

129 A pallet converter is a frame (usually metal) which fits onto a wooden pallet to enable crushable or unevenly shaped loads to be stacked. They are widely used in cold stores. The pallet converter should be rigid even without a load or with a part load and reliance should not be placed on a full load to ensure rigidity.

130 Locking pins or other devices used to locate and lock the converter onto the pallet must be in good working order and free from defect. To ensure that pallet converters are in a condition to be stacked safely, there should be an effective system of control over pallets and component parts of converters to ensure that all the component parts are compatible with each other. Damaged or defective pallet converters should not be used.

## TROLLIES OR ROLL CONTAINERS
(See Figure 16)

131 These are very common pieces of equipment, but care is required in the selection of a suitable design,

ie without any projecting hinges, clips or castors, which could cause injury. Used properly they are a convenient means of conveying goods from one area to another. However, they are very open to misuse. The main dangers arise from:

(a) overloading the trolley (including top heavy loading) making it more difficult to control;

(b) trapping fingers in the open mesh sides;

(c) trapping limbs between the trolley and fixed structures;

(d) running over toes;

(e) people being struck or trapped by a trolley rolling down a gradient.

132 Trollies are designed to be used on level even surfaces. If used on a gradient there may be a risk of trollies free-wheeling out of control and causing injury to people. Trollies should not therefore be generally used on gradients unless a safe system of work is adopted to prevent such risks from occurring. In addition, careful consideration may need to be given to the corresponding increase in manual effort required (see under Manual Handling section).

133 Staff using this type of equipment should be properly trained in its correct use and regular checks should be made to ensure that it is not being mis-used. Trollies should be the subject of regular checks to ensure that they are in good working order. This should ensure defective trollies are taken out of service and returned for repair. Consideration should be given to the provision of safety footwear when using trollies.

## RACKING SYSTEMS

134 The term 'racking' is used to describe a skeleton framework of fixed or adjustable design to support loads without the use of shelves. It is usually qualified (pallet racking, tyre racking, drum racking, for example). Racking systems are widely used in warehouses as there are space advantages over floor storage and they provide for easy access and retrieval of goods. There are many different types of racking system. The most common types found in warehouses are described in Table 5. Table 6 lists terms used for racking systems.

135 The glossary of terms and certain definitions used in this section have been reproduced with kind permission from the Storage Equipment Manufacturers Association (SEMA) publication *Recommended practice for the use of static racking* (see Appendix 5).

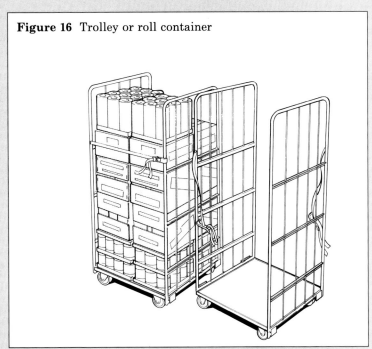

**Figure 16** Trolley or roll container

**Table 5** Common types of racking system used in warehouses

| Type of racking | Description |
|---|---|
| 1 **Adjustable pallet racking** | A system of upright frames connected by horizontal beams to provide pallet storage levels, which can be adjusted vertically. |
| 2 **Mobile racking** | A system where the racking is mounted on movable base frames running on rails. Can be power operated, manually operated or mechanically assisted. |
| 3 **Cantilever racking** | Racking incorporating cantilever arms, fixed or adjustable. |
| 4 **Live storage racking** | A live storage system provides a block of storage in depth, which has a rear or 'loading face' and a front or 'picking face'. Goods are conveyed from the loading to the picking face, either by gravity, using an inclined surface or track, or by horizontal powered conveyor. So, only two aisles are necessary to service a block of storage whatever the depth. |
| 5 **Drive through and drive in pallet rackin** | This system provides blocks of static storage where pallets are stored two or more deep. By driving into the bay, access is gained to pallets, supported along their sides on beam rails cantilevered from the frames. (a) Drive in system: The lift truck drives into a bay and reverses out. (b) Drive through: Similar to drive in but truck may drive through the block from one aisle to another. |

**Table 6** Glossary of terms used in adjustable pallet racking systems

| Term | Description |
|------|-------------|
| 1 Bay | A module between upright frames. |
| 2 Run | A series of bays connected lengthwise. |
| 3 Single side run | Single depth of rack, usually accessible from one side only. |
| 4 Double sided run | Two runs built back to back. |
| 5 Levels | Number of storage levels in the height. |
| 6 Aisle | Space giving access to picking or loading faces. |
| 7 Gangway | Space for movement or transport but not giving direct access to picking or loading faces. |
| 8 Frame | Two or more uprights, joined by bracing members. |
| 9 Base plate | Fitted to base of upright for floor fixing, or load spreading. |
| 10 Beam | Horizontal load carrying member. May be fitted with a connector at each end for engagement with frame upright at predetermined increments, or by using clamps to permit infinite vertical adjustment. |
| 11 Run spacer | A member connecting and spacing two back to back runs. |
| 12 Beam connector lock | A device for preventing accidental removal of beams. Can be integral part of the beam or a separate component. |
| 13 Wall tie | A fixing between rack and wall to provide spacing and/or stability. |
| 14 Pallet stop | A component positioned at the rear to ensure that a pallet spans the beam correctly. (*Note*: Use *not* recommended - see paragraph 138) |
| 15 Block - when used to describe: | |
| (a) mobile racking; | consists of a number of mobile runs usually with one aisle; |
| (b) live storage racking; | a number of connected bays, each providing storage in depth; |
| (c) drive through/ drive in. | consists of a number of connected bays. |

136 All racking systems should be of good mechanical construction, sound materials, adequate strength and installed and maintained in accordance with the manufacturer's instructions. The maximum load for any installation should be conspicuously marked on it.

### Racking installation

137 The requirements for the safe installation of racking vary according to the type and size of the system, and the nature of the building or area for which it is intended. Safe working loads, heights, widths and equipment tolerances should be set by the designers and manufacturers of the total system. The basic principles for safe installation are as follows:

(a) racking should be installed in accordance with the manufacturer's instructions;

(b) racking should be erected on sound, level floors, capable of withstanding the point loading at each base plate;

(c) where the design of the racking requires it to be secured to the building, only those building members which have been 'proved' by structural calculations should be used. It therefore follows that the design of the racking in such a case should be compatible with the building layout;

(d) double sided runs should be connected and spaced using suitable run spacers;

(e) where necessary, for example where lift trucks or other mechanical handling equipment are used, racking should be securely fixed to the floor (see paragraphs 139-140);

(f) aisles should be wide enough to ensure that mechanical handling equipment can be easily manoeuvred. Widths will depend very much on the type of equipment used, for example some require a 90° turn to load and off-load, some remain parallel to the aisle and have forks at 90° to the direction of travel;

(g) beam connector locks should always be securely fixed at the ends of each beam, when adjustable pallet racking is installed, to prevent accidental displacement of beams, for example by lift truck;

(h) racking should have securely fixed to it a clear unambiguous notice stating its maximum load together with any necessary specified load configurations. See the SEMA publication *Recommended practice for the use of static racking* (see Appendix 5).

(i) the limitations indicated in the maximum load notice should never be exceeded. The weight of each palletised load should be established before a decision is made to store it in the racking. This is particularly important where multi-products are stored which may vary considerably in weight or where a new line of product is brought into the warehouse for the first time. In some situations it may not be necessary to establish the weight of each palletised load, if the racking system is designed and installed to meet the requirements of storage of the heaviest palletised load in the company's operation. Nevertheless, a system must be adopted by the employer to ensure that all palletised loads intended for storage in racking can be safely stored in accordance with the particular racking design and installation;

(j) racking should never be altered, for example by welding, nor components removed without first consulting the manufacturer. Before changing the position of adjustable components on racking as supplied, the employer should establish the design limitations of the new configuration and, where necessary, amend the safe working load notice;

(k) high visible colours for key components of the racking, for example horizontal beams, will assist lift truck drivers to correctly position the forks and avoid damage.

### Pallet stops

138 The use of pallet stops attached to racking structures may increase the risk of structural damage from the load or thrust that may be applied to the racking when a palletised load is placed into or retrieved from the racking. If racking layouts are correctly designed to give adequate clearance between back to back pallets or loads then pallet stops are unnecessary for a trained and competent driver to deposit a pallet correctly and safely.

### Racking stability

139 The main factors that influence the stability of racking installations are the height-to-depth ratio and whether they are fixed to the floor or other suitable parts of the building's structure. Free standing racks, ie not fixed to the floor, should not be used where lift trucks or other mechanical handling devices are used.

140 Where racks are subjected to superimposed loads, plus horizontal forces from loading and unloading, the minimum requirements for floor fixing should be:

(a) floor fix uprights adjacent to aisles and gangways, where the height/depth ratio does not exceed 6:1;

(b) floor fix all uprights, where the height/depth ratio exceeds 6:1 but does not exceed 10:1.

However, in order to provide an increased safety factor, many users of racking consider it prudent to secure all uprights to the floor. Floor fixing should be such that the anticipated horizontal shear and vertical tensile forces can be safely resisted. Where the height/depth ratio exceeds 10:1 specialist advice should be sought from the manufacturer. Drive-in and drive-through racks should always be designed and floor fixed according to the manufacturers' instructions.

### Protection of racking

141 Where racking is likely to be struck by lift trucks and other vehicles it should be protected. Renewable column guards or guide rails should be used to prevent the truck getting too close to the main structure. Corner uprights are especially at risk and should be carefully protected and painted in a conspicuous colour.

### Racking maintenance

142 In general, racking is manufactured from relatively lightweight materials and, as a consequence, there is a limit to the amount of abuse that it can withstand. The skill of lift truck operators has a great bearing on the amount of damage likely to be caused. Any damage to racking will reduce its load carrying capacity. The greater the damage the less its strength will be, until it will eventually collapse, even when supporting its normal working load.

143 To ensure that a racking installation continues to be serviceable and safe it is recommended that:

(a) regular planned inspections of racking are carried out to identify and determine the extent of any damage and any necessary remedial action to be taken; and

(b) staff are encouraged to report any damage, however minor, so that its effect on safety can be assessed;

(c) the contents of the maximum load notice be strictly adhered to; and

(d) the racking manufacturer be contacted for advice if there is any uncertainty as to the integrity of the racking system;

(e) a log book should be kept for recording inspections, damage and repairs.

Note: Where damage is identified that affects the safety

of the racking system, the racking should be offloaded and controls introduced to prevent it being used until remedial repair work has been carried out.

## PLACING AND RETRIEVING STOCK FROM RACKING AND SHELVING

144 Manual handling of goods and stock should be avoided wherever possible (see under Manual Handling section). In most warehouses mechanical handling devices, for example lift trucks, are used to place and retrieve stock from racking (see under Manual Handling section).

145 Where it is necessary to place or retrieve stock from racking by hand, the following basic principles should be adopted:

(a) access to the racking or shelving should be by means other than climbing the racking or shelving;

(b) free standing mobile platform steps should be used in preference to ordinary ladders;

(c) where steps and ladders are used they should conform to British Standards, for example BS 1129:1982 for timber ladders and steps, BS 2037:1984 for aluminium ladders and steps - see Appendix 5;

(d) where single section ladders are used they should be provided with hooks and other devices at the upper end to fix on to the racking to prevent the ladder from slipping or twisting when in use. Such devices should only be used where the racking has been designed to accommodate the forces likely to be imposed on it.

(e) Ladders should be individually identified, checked before and after use and examined regularly by a competent person. Ladders found to be defective should be suitably labelled and withdrawn from service until repaired. A record should be kept of these inspections;

(f) mechanical handling plant should not be permitted to operate in aisles where personnel are engaged in such operations.

Further information on the safe use of ladders can be found in HSE Guidance Note GS 31 *Safe use of ladders, step ladders and trestles* (see Appendix 5).

## GENERAL

146 In almost all warehouses manual handling operations (ie transporting or supporting a load by hand or by bodily force - including lifting, putting down, pushing, pulling, carrying or moving) will be undertaken. Manual handling accidents account for more than a third of all reported accidents in warehouses.

147 Manual handling tasks involve a risk of strains and sprains, notably to the back, but also to other parts of the body. The chance of a back disorder developing is increased when handling involves heavy loads, is prolonged, frequent or combined with awkward postures. The stresses within the body vary with the rate of application of force, and with the bodily posture adopted. What may be safe when carried out slowly and smoothly may be dangerous if carried out jerkily and quickly in an unstable posture. What may be safe in the erect posture may be dangerous when stooping. A given force may be acceptable if it is applied only once within a day, and be dangerous if it has to be applied repeatedly. Because of the variation in physical dimensions, for example height and reach, and strength of individuals, what may be acceptable for one employee to handle may be unacceptable for another. It can be seen, therefore, that the weight of an object, while being an important factor, is not the only factor to consider in manual handling operations, and setting weight limits would be too simple a solution to the problem.

148 In May 1990 the European Communities adopted a Directive on manual handling. In brief, the Directive requires employers to avoid the need for manual handling where there is a risk of injury or, where this is not possible, to assess their manual handling operations and take appropriate steps to avoid or reduce that risk. The Directive must be implemented by 31 December 1992 and it will be implemented in the United Kingdom through Regulations supported by general guidance.

149 It should not be forgotten that handling tasks carry additional risks of injury from slips, trips or falls, striking against objects, cuts, trapping of limbs or extremities etc.

## PREVENTION OR CONTROL OF RISK

150 Risks from manual handling operations are best avoided by the elimination of such operations. In warehouses where this is impracticable, manual handling should be minimised as far as is reasonably possible. Employers should consider all systems of work in the warehouse involving manual handling operations and, where appropriate, redesign tasks to:

(a) avoid the need to move loads manually;

(b) fully utilise mechanical handling devices, for example lift trucks, pallet trucks, trolleys, conveyors, chutes, scissor lifts (see Manual Handling section).

Where necessary additional mechanical handling devices should be introduced to avoid or reduce manual handling operations.

### Assessment

151 Where hazardous manual handling operations cannot be avoided, the employer should make an assessment of all such operations likely to be carried out in the warehouse. The assessment should identify where improvements or other measures are necessary to reduce the risk of injury from manual handling operations. The following factors should be considered when making such an assessment.

(a) *The task:*
Are there any tasks which involve foreseeable risks? For example unsatisfactory bodily movements or posture; excessive lifting or lowering distances, for example from floor level to above waist height; excessive pushing or pulling distances, or situations where the load is required to be held or manipulated at a distance from the trunk (see Figures 17 and 18).

(b) *The load:*
Are there any loads unsuitable for manual handling? For example, too heavy, bulky, slippery, wet, sharp, unknown offset centres of gravity, unstable or contents likely to shift.

(c) *The working environment:*
Are there any areas of the warehouse unsuitable for manual handling operations? For example constricted work areas, narrow aisles, areas of extreme temperature (hot or cold), over-steep slopes or changes in floor level.

(d) *Individual person's capability:*
Are there any employees unsuitable for manual handling operations? For example pregnant workers, people with known medical conditions.

MANUAL
HANDLING

31

**Figure 17** Good lifting technique

(a) Plan the lift

(b) Determine the best lifting technique

(c) Get a secure grip

(d) Pull the load in close to your body

**Figure 18** Poor manual handling practices

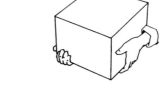

(a) Avoid above shoulder reach

(b) Avoid forward bending

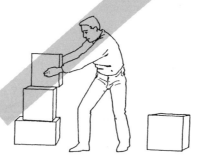

(c) Avoid twisting of the back

(d) Avoid sideways bending of the back

**Figure 19** Examples of modifying workplace layout

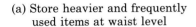

(a) Store heavier and frequently
used items at waist level

*Before*          *After*

(b) Raise work level by use of self-adjusting platform

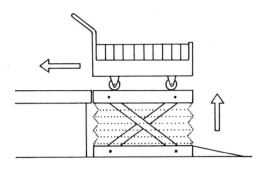

(c) Adjustable height platform
reduces lifting

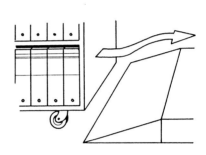

(d) Ramps avoid lifting
or dragging

*Poor*                    *Better*

(e) Adjustable work heights

152 Where assessment identifies manual handling operations that involve risk of injury appropriate measures should be taken to reduce those risks as far as is reasonably practicable, for example by redesign of the task or system of work, alteration of shelving heights or layout of the warehouses or introduction of mechanical handling devices to assist in the operation (see Figure 19).

**TEAM HANDLING**

153 Handling by two or more people introduces additional problems which an assessment should consider. During the handling operation the proportion of the load that is borne by each member of the team will inevitably vary to some extent. Therefore, the load that a team can handle in safety is less than the sum of the loads that the individual team members could cope with when working alone. As an approximate guide the safe capacity of a two person team is two thirds of the sum of their individual capacities; and for a three person team the safe capacity is half the sum of their individual capacities. Additional difficulties may arise if team members impede each other's vision or movement.

## INFORMATION AND TRAINING

154 Where it is reasonably practicable to do so employers should give workers precise information about the weight of a load and, where the centre of gravity is not centrally positioned, the location of the heaviest side of the load, perhaps by ensuring that the weight and/or the heaviest side is clearly marked on the load itself. Where this is not done employers should give workers a general indication of the weights and centres of gravity of the range of loads to be handled, sufficient to make workers aware of the potential risks.

155 Employers should also ensure that their employees clearly understand how a manual handling operation has been designed to safeguard their health and safety. Training should complement a safe system of work and not be a substitute for it. A training programme should provide a clear understanding of:

(a) how potentially hazardous loads may be recognised;

(b) how to deal with unfamiliar loads;

(c) the proper use of handling aids;

(d) the proper use of personal protective equipment;

(e) features of the working environment that contribute to safety;

(f) the importance of good housekeeping;

(g) factors affecting individual capability;

(h) good handling techniques.

156 Use this check-list to assess manual handling.

## CHECK-LIST FOR EMPLOYERS

- Have you organised work in the warehouse to eliminate or minimise hazardous manual handling operations?

- Have you assessed those handling tasks that cannot be avoided?

- Can mechanical systems be introduced?

- Can the loads be improved? Can they be made smaller, lighter, more portable? Can handles be provided? Can you improve the external state of the loads, for example smooth off jagged edges? Can loads be marked to show how or where to hold them?

- Can handling aids be employed, such as trolleys, slides, and chutes, or conveyors? Is personal protective equipment necessary?

Is equipment properly maintained and accessible?

- Can the workplace or task be redesigned to reduce bending, twisting, stretching, carrying distances, frequency of handling? Can jobs be rotated to avoid repetition and constant exertion? Is proper allowance made for rest pauses?

- Can the workplace be made safer by widening gangways, removing obstructions, keeping floors clean, providing proper lighting and temperature control?

- Has allowance been made for individual characteristics of the workforce?

- Is instruction and training necessary? If a training programme is introduced, is its effectiveness being monitored?

- Do any of the tasks require special strength or fitness? If so, has this been properly evaluated and employees selected accordingly? Are the effects being monitored?

## GENERAL

157 Mechanical handling devices are used extensively to move materials and goods into, out of, and inside warehouse premises. Lift trucks, order picking machines, scissor lifts, conveyors, teagles and overhead travelling cranes are common examples of such devices. It should be noted that there are a number of EC directives which will lead to the implementation of UK legislation which may affect some of the content of this chapter.

## LIFT TRUCKS

158 Lift trucks (LTs) are designed to lift loads, move and re-stack them in a different place. The common types of LT found in warehouse premises are illustrated in Figures 20-24. LTs are usually powered by electric batteries or by an internal combustion engine (LPG, diesel or petrol).

159 LTs account for a large proportion of accidents in warehouses. Many of these accidents are due to operator error associated with inadequate or lack of training. There are, however, other reasons for LT accidents, including unsuitable premises, poor layout and design of LT operating areas and poor truck maintenance. Employers using LTs should therefore adopt safe systems of work, for example procedures for training employees, for traffic and pedestrian movement, and for control and maintenance of trucks.

## DESIGN FEATURES OF REACH, COUNTERBALANCED AND VERY NARROW AISLE TRUCKS

160 All trucks supplied after 1 January 1989 must comply with the Self-Propelled Industrial Trucks (EEC Requirements) Regulations 1988 and must display an EC conformity mark to show that they comply with the requirements laid down in EC Directive 86/663/EEC relating to self-propelled industrial trucks.

161 The following points apply to all trucks. The following information should be displayed on the truck:

(a) the name of the manufacturer (or importer) of the truck;

(b) truck type;

(c) serial number;

(d) unladen weight (electric lift trucks are shown without the battery weight which is marked on its own plate);

(e) rated capacity;

(f) load centre distance;

**Figure 20** Reach truck. A lift truck whose design enables the load to be retracted within the wheel base. This minimises the overall working length and allows the aisle width to be reduced.

(g) maximum lift height;

(h) inflation pressures (if pneumatic tyres are fitted).

162 The LT should be fitted with:

(a) brakes (service and parking) capable of holding the truck and its maximum permissible load when parked;

(b) a safety lock or switch with removable key to prevent unauthorised use;

(c) a clearly audible warning device (horn);

(d) an overhead guard, of sufficient strength to protect the operator from falling objects;

(e) guards to prevent access to dangerous moving parts, for example telescopic mast sections which are within the operator's reach in normal operating position.

MECHANICAL HANDLING

35

**Figure 21** Counterbalanced lift truck. The name is derived from the fact that loads placed on the forks are counterbalanced by the weight of the vehicle over the rear wheels.

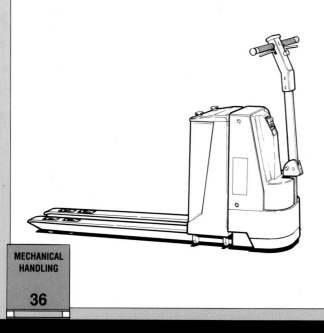

**Figure 22** Pallet truck. This truck has two elevating fingers for insertion below the top deck of a pallet. When the fingers are raised the load is moved clear of the ground to allow movement. This truck may be designed for pedestrian or rider control. It has no mast and cannot be used for stacking. Pallet trucks may be powered or non-powered.

163 The following additional safety measures may also be necessary:

(a) a load back rest, if the LT is used to move small objects liable to fall on the operator;

(b) lights, if the LT is used in drive in or drive through racking, or in other poorly lit areas;

(c) it may be desirable to equip the LT with a flashing warning beacon and/or automatic reverse warning device.

164 The risk of loads falling from the truck can be reduced by the use of suitable attachments, for example fork extensions or barrel clamps. In all cases the manufacturers of the LT should be consulted about the suitability of the attachment for a particular truck.

## FITTING ATTACHMENTS

165 Fitting an attachment such as a side shift or clamp will affect the rated capacity of the truck. Reducing the rated capacity of the truck to account for the effect of fitting an attachment is called derating. Derating should be carried out by an authorised dealer or the original truck manufacturer. Lift truck operators will require additional training on the use of such attachments.

## TRAINING OF LIFT TRUCK OPERATORS

166 The Approved Code of Practice *Rider operated lift trucks - operator training* (see Appendix 5) is directed at the basic training of all employees whose employment after 1 April 1989 includes for the first time the operation of rider operated LTs of the four types most commonly used (including reach and counterbalanced LTs). However, to comply with their duties under the Health and Safety at Work etc Act employers must ensure that *all* operators they employ, both new and existing, are adequately trained and competent. Therefore, no person should be permitted to operate an LT unless properly trained, competent and authorised in writing by the employer to do so. The authorisation should only be given for the type or types of truck for which training has been successfully completed.

167 Employers should be careful in selecting potential LT operators. Those selected should be:

(a) reliable;
(b) able to do the job;
(c) responsible in their attitude;
(d) physically capable;
(e) have good eyesight and hearing;
(f) over 17 years old.

Note: The HSE booklet *Safety in working with lift trucks* (currently being revised) will give a comprehensive guide to medical assessments and the types of illness which may debar a person from driving an LT.

168 The training of operators should be carried out by a competent person and always include three stages:

- basic training - the basic skills and knowledge required for safe operation;

- specific job training - knowledge of workplace and experience of any special needs and handling attachments;

- familiarisation training - operation on-the-job under close competent supervision.

169 The first two stages may be combined or integrated but should always be off-the-job. The employer should keep a record for each employee who has satisfactorily completed any stage of LT training. This should include sufficient information to identify the employee, the nature of training completed and copies or details of any certificate of training.

170 Successful training is dependent on the competence of the instructor who should be asked to supply evidence of training and experience both as an instructor and as an operator. The Health and Safety Commission has recognised four bodies as competent to operate voluntary accreditation schemes. This should help employers to select training organisations or LT suppliers offering a good standard of training. The recognised accrediting bodies are:

- The Agricultural Training Board.
- Construction Industry Training Board.
- The Road Transport Industry Training Board.
- The Association of Industrial Truck Trainers.

171 For further information on training of LT operators see the Approved Code of Practice *Rider operated lift trucks - operator training* (see Appendix 5).

## PROTECTION OF PUBLIC, EMPLOYEES AND VISITING DRIVERS

172(a) *The public*. Members of the public should not be permitted in LT operating areas. Where members of the public visit warehouse premises the following general precautions should be adopted:

(i) provide sufficient clear and unambiguous warning signs at strategic locations to inform people that LTs operate in the premises or area (see Figure 25);

(ii) define, designate and clearly mark pedestrian routes and crossing places;

(iii) provide suitable barriers to segregate the public from LT operating areas.

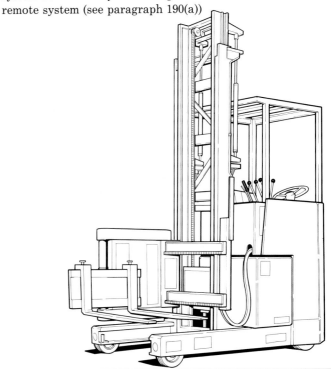

**Figure 23** Very narrow aisle truck. These trucks do not have to turn within the working aisle to deposit and retrieve loads. They are ideal for long runs down very narrow aisles. Some are fitted with a rotating head and can serve both sides of an aisle without the need for the truck to turn round. Very narrow aisle trucks may be guided by truck and rails in the floor or at the base of the racks or by an automatic steering system controlled by a buried guidance wire or other remote system (see paragraph 190(a))

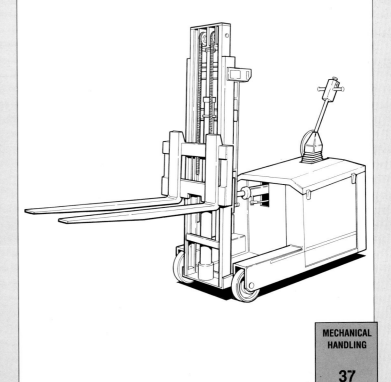

**Figure 24** Pallet stacker truck. May be pedestrian operated or ride-on. They may be equipped with a battery powered lift facility or the lift may be made using hydraulic hand pump.

**Figure 25** Warning sign that lift trucks operate (black with a yellow background)

(b) *Employees*. Wherever possible, access to lift truck operating areas should be restricted to those staff who operate LT equipment or have a supervisory role. The same general precautions as listed above for members of the public may be appropriate to protect employees who do not normally have to enter LT operating areas. Where employees work in conjunction with LTs, the following general precautions should be adopted:

(i) provide sufficient clear and unambiguous warning signs at strategic locations to inform employees that LTs operate in the premises or area (see Figure 25);

(ii) provide suitable and sufficient notices at strategic locations and instructing LT operators to sound the horn of the LT;

(iii) use LTs with flashing warning beacons;

(iv) instruct employees to stand clear of LTs that are lifting or lowering loads and to use separate walkways where provided. People should be reminded of the dangers of entering areas such as those behind the LT where they may not be fully visible to the driver;

(v) provide and instruct LT operators and employees to wear footwear (to BS 1870 - see Appendix 5), and where there is a forseeable risk of head injury from falling objects, safety helmets (to BS 5240 - see Appendix 5). A further useful precaution would be the provision of high visibility clothing or light coloured overalls. Provision of such clothing should be in accordance with the requirements of the Personal Protective Equipment Regulations which come into force on 1 January 1993.

(c) *Visiting drivers*. Where a lorry is being loaded or unloaded close to the cab, an assessment should be made of the risk to the driver and any passenger of injury from goods or materials collapsing onto the cab or forks piercing it. The potential risk is affected by features such as the direction of loading (side/back), type of load, lorry design etc. Where a risk is identified, a designated safe reception/waiting area should be provided and the cab occupants directed to it. A further useful precaution would be the provision of high visibility clothing or light coloured overalls if visiting drivers are in areas where there may be a risk of them being struck.

**LIFT TRUCK OPERATING AREAS**

173 All LT operating areas should be suitably designed and properly maintained. When designing the layout of LT operating areas the following points should be considered:

(a) driving areas should be as flat as possible and free from obstructions. Features of the building or operating area, for example support columns, pipework or other plant, should be identified, protected and clearly marked by black and yellow diagonal stripes. The edges of loading bays should be clearly marked in a similar way;

(b) roads, gangways and aisles should have sufficient width and overhead clearance for the largest LT using them to do so safely, whether loaded or unloaded, and if necessary to allow other vehicles and loads to pass each other in safety. If speed retarders (sleeping policemen) are used to reduce the speed of other traffic, a by-pass will need to be provided for use by LTs. One-way traffic systems should be considered to reduce the risk of collisions;

(c) buildings, rooms, doorways, and traffic routes should be clearly marked to avoid unnecessary traffic movements;

(d) sharp bends and overhead obstructions should be avoided;

(e) notices instructing LT operators to sound horns at appropriate locations should be displayed. All warning signs should conform to the Safety Signs Regulations;

(f) lighting should be arranged to avoid glare - for example flexible doors of transparent or translucent material will reflect like a mirror if it is appreciably darker on one side of the door than on the other - and sudden changes of lighting levels, for example where LTs may pass from bright sunlight into the building;

(g) sufficient parking areas should be provided for all LTs. Parking areas should be away from the main thoroughfare and work areas. Where parking areas are used for recharging or refuelling further considerations are necessary (see paragraphs 180-182).

## CONTROL OF THE USE OF LTS

174 Keys should be kept in a secure place when the LT is not in use. They should be issued only to authorised operators and retained by them until the end of the work period. On completion of work LTs should be parked in the designated parking area with the engine switched off, fork arms lowered flat to the ground and the brake applied. On battery operated trucks the battery should be disconnected. On LPG powered trucks the gas supply should be turned off at the cylinder.

## BASIC RULES FOR LIFT TRUCK OPERATORS

175 The following simple rules should always be applied by operators of warehouse reach and counterbalanced LTs. Where appropriate these rules should be followed by the operators of other types of LTs. These rules are not intended to be a substitute for the often extensive guidance available from LT manufacturers.

NEVER:

- lift loads which exceed the truck's rated capacity;

- travel forwards with a bulky load obscuring vision;

- travel on soft ground unless the LT is suitable for this purpose;

- carry passengers;

- block fire-fighting equipment or exits by parking or stacking in front of it;

- attempt to carry out repairs - leave this to a qualified maintenance engineer;

- use attachments unless:

  (i) derating (ie reducing the rated capacity of the LT) has been carried out by a competent and authorised dealer or manufacturer;

  (ii) operators have been properly trained and are competent and authorised to use the truck with the attachment; and

  (iii) the attachment is used in accordance with the manufacturer's instructions.

- allow people to walk under a raised mast or load;

- travel with a raised load;

- attempt to turn on an incline.

ALWAYS:

- observe floor loading limits - find out the weight of the laden truck;

- watch out for obstructions;

- ensure the load is not wider than the width of the gangways;

- when driving on inclines ensure that:

  (i) when carrying the load, it faces uphill;

  (ii) when no load is carried, the fork arms face downhill;

  (iii) where fitted, the tilt is adjusted to suit the gradient and the fork arms are raised to provide ground clearance;

- avoid sudden stops;

- slow down for corners and sound horn where appropriate;

- travel with fork arms lowered while maintaining ground clearance;

- ensure that bridge plates are secure and strong to withstand the weight of the truck and the load;

- carry out a pre-shift check of the LT (see paragraph 176);

- lower loads as soon as they are clear of the racking;

- lower heavy loads slowly;

- leave the truck with the fork arms fully lowered;

- switch off and remove the key when leaving the truck;

- take note of the load capacity indicator when fitted.

REMEMBER:

- never allow unauthorised people to operate the LT.

Further advice on the safe operation of LTs can be found in the HSE publication *Safety in working with lift trucks* (see Appendix 5).

## MAINTENANCE AND EXAMINATION OF LTS

176 Employers should have:

(a) a system for reporting defects and for ensuring that remedial work is carried out;

(b) a planned routine maintenance system.

Manufacturer's instructions on inspection, maintenance and servicing should be followed. The operator, unless suitably qualified and authorised, should not carry out repairs and adjustments to the truck. If a truck is hired, arrangements should be made to ensure proper inspection, maintenance and servicing. (In some cases, the hire company may undertake regular inspection, maintenance and servicing as part of the hire contract). The employer should keep a written record of six monthly examinations (see paragraph 178).

### Daily maintenance

177 At the beginning of each shift, check that:

(a) tyre pressures are correct and tyres are not damaged, for example by nails or cuts;

(b) parking and service brakes operate efficiently;

(c) audible warning signal works;

(d) lights, if fitted, work;

(e) fluid levels, for example fuel, water, lubricating oil and hydraulic oil levels are correct in internal combustion engined LTs;

(f) where appropriate, batteries of LTs are adequately charged;

(g) systems for lifting, tilting and manipulation are working properly.

### Weekly maintenance (50 hours or the period recommended by the manufacturer)

178 Trucks should be checked by a person authorised for the purpose. Checks should include:

(a) all daily checks;

(b) operation of steering gear, lifting gear and other working parts;

(c) condition of the mast, forks, attachments and any chains or ropes used in the lifting mechanisms;

(d) checking hydraulic cylinders and hoses for signs of damage and leaks.

179 A written report should be made of the condition of the LT: if it is unsafe to use the fault(s) should be rectified immediately or the LT should be withdrawn from service. These reports should be retained by the employer until the next six-monthly examination.

### Six-monthly examination (1000 running hours or the period recommended by the manufacturer)

180 All working parts of the truck, including the chains or ropes, should be thoroughly examined at least once every six months. Such examinations should be carried out by a competent person, for example insurance company engineer or

manufacturer. A certificate should be issued by the examiner that the truck is free from patent defect. The certificate should be retained by the employer for at least six months. Where the examination shows that the truck is unsafe to use, it should be taken out of service until the necessary remedial repairs can be carried out. The truck should then be re-examined before being taken back into use.

## REFUELLING OF LIFT TRUCKS

181 Areas used for refuelling LTs should be outside the warehouse. Refuelling should not take place where there is a likelihood of an accumulation of flammable vapours in the event of a spillage, for example pits, gulleys etc. Guidance on the storage of flammable liquids in tanks and containers can be found in the HSE booklets *The storage of flammable liquids in fixed tanks (up to 10 000 m³ total capacity)* and *The storage of flammable liquids in containers* - (see Appendix 5). The local Fire Authority will advise on the standard necessary to comply with the Petroleum (Consolidation) Act 1928 and in the guidance given in *The storage of flammable liquids in fixed tanks (up to 10 000 m³ total capacity)* and *The storage of flammable liquids in containers* (see Appendix 5). Notices prohibiting smoking should be clearly displayed in these areas and engines should be switched off before refuelling.

182 The cylinders of LPG fuelled LTs should be changed outside the warehouse away from all possible sources of ignition. Guidance on the storage of LPG cylinders can be found in the HSE Guidance Note *Keeping of LPG in cylinders and similar containers* - see Appendix 5.

183 If the LT is fitted with integral tanks or employers refill their own cylinders the installation should be outside the warehouse and comply with HSE's booklet *Storage of LPG at fixed installations* (see Appendix 5). Further information on LPG refuelling facilities can be found in the *Liquefied Petroleum Gas Industry Technical Association (LPGITA) Code of Practice 20* (see Appendix 5). LPG refilling installations, including cylinders that are refilled, must comply with the requirements of the Pressure Systems and Transportable Gas Container Regulations 1989 and the Approved Code of Practice.

## CHARGING OF BATTERIES OF ELECTRICALLY POWERED LIFT TRUCKS

184 During the charging of lead-acid batteries hydrogen is evolved from the cells and there is a risk of fire and/or explosion if flammable mixtures of hydrogen with air accumulate. The acid also presents a hazard to skin and eyes. Face masks or goggles, protective aprons, gloves and emergency eye washing facilities should be provided whenever

there is a risk of splashing, for example during acid dilution or battery filling etc.

185 The following general precautions should be adopted:

(a) a separate room or area should be designated for charging of batteries;

(b) charging rooms or areas should have good ventilation located at high level immediately above the batteries;

(c) electrical apparatus and any other potential sources of ignition should be kept well to one side and/or sited below the level of the battery, but not in a position where any spillage of electrolyte could fall onto the electrical apparatus;

(d) the area should be designated 'No smoking' and 'No naked lights';

(e) to avoid sparks the charger should be switched off before the battery is connected to or disconnected from it.

## USE OF LIFT TRUCKS WHERE FLAMMABLE MATERIALS MAY BE PRESENT

186 There are two main hazards associated with the use of LTs in flammable atmospheres:

(a) direct ignition of the surrounding flammable atmosphere, for example by hot surfaces, unprotected electrical equipment or hot sparks from the exhaust);

(b) ingestion of a flammable atmosphere into the air intake of the engine. If this happens, the engine is liable to accelerate out of control causing overspeeding, possible flashback through the intake, to ignite the surrounding flammable atmosphere.

For these reasons LTs should not be used in areas where flammable vapour, gases or dusts are liable to be present, unless they have been suitably designed and equipped for such use.

187 Diesel-fuelled trucks may be used providing certain precautions are being taken. (See HSE's Guidance Note *Diesel engined lift trucks in hazardous areas* (see Appendix 5). Petrol and LPG-fuelled trucks should not be used because they cannot, as yet, be protected for such use. If there is any doubt about the suitability of an LT for use in such circumstances, advice should be sought from the manufacturer or local HSE Area Office before it is used.

## WORKING PLATFORMS ON LIFT TRUCKS

188 Although the primary function of an LT is the carriage, raising and lowering of articles, its use as a working platform may present advantages over other means of access to heights, such as a ladder, for example when access to building structures or racking etc may be necessary. Even so, it is recommended that a specifically designed mobile elevating working platform be used instead of such an LT. If, however an ordinary LT is used in conjunction with a working platform, the safety of the unit as a whole (truck and platform) should be considered. The following safeguards should be adopted.

(a) Before using an LT for the first time to carry a working platform it is essential to seek the advice of the truck manufacturer or supplier to confirm that the truck design is suitable for this purpose, for the proposed platform design, and for the method of securing the platform to the truck.

(b) The platform design should meet the standards set out in paragraphs 7,8,9 and 10 of the HSE Guidance Note *Working platforms on forklift trucks* (see Appendix 5).

(c) The platform should be effectively secured to the LT's elevating carriage.

(d) All platform edges should be guarded by:

(i) a top rail (900 mm to 1100 mm from the platform floor);

(ii) a toe board (minimum height 100 mm);

(iii) an intermediate rail or total enclosure between the top rail and toe board.

(e) Guards should be provided to prevent people reaching any dangerous moving parts of the LT, for example where a chain passes over a sprocket.

(f) Where there are overhead hazards against which people could be crushed, for example roof structures, pipework etc, suitable overhead protection for people on the platform should be provided.

(g) Consideration should be given to arranging controls so that the raising and lowering of the platform can be controlled by the person on the platform or a platform-mounted emergency stop lifting control should be provided. Where this is not reasonably practicable, suitable means of communication between the truck operator and the person on the platform must be provided. Where manual signals are used, clear and unambiguous signals must be agreed and understood *before* beginning work.

(h) As a general rule, no person should be in an elevated position when the LT is travelling. However, provided a travel motion emergency stop device is fitted on the platform, small positioning movements may be made at creep speed (2.5 km/h max). This travel control should be suitably interlocked to ensure that this speed

**Figure 26** Guided rail/free hanging order picking machine

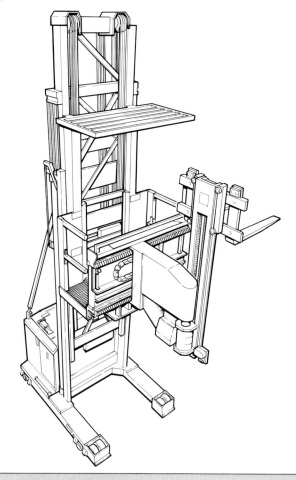

cannot be exceeded while the platform is in an elevated position.

(i)   Any work carried out from the platform should be as far as is reasonably practicable within the area bounded by the guard rails and be such that people do not need to lean out beyond the platform. LTs fitted with a working platform should not be used as a substitute for an order picking truck.

(j)   LT operators and people working on a platform should be properly trained, given full instructions and information on a safe system of work and be competent to carry out the given task.

(k)   No more than two people should be carried on the platform.

## ORDER PICKING MACHINES (OPMS)

189 OPMs are used to transfer goods and materials to and from racking or storage systems by providing the operator with a place to deposit items that have been picked, and usually a platform or cage to facilitate reaching higher levels (see Figure 26).

190 There are various basic types of OPM and these include:

(a)   free ranging - steered by the operator at all times and not normally intended for use within

narrow aisles (ie those aisles whose width exceeds the width of the OPM by not more than 300 mm);

(b)   guided rail/free ranging - can operate within narrow aisles and open areas. Rollers on the sides of the OPM engage with low level guide rails fitted to the racking to provide lateral restraint;

(c)   guided and supported by track/rail (commonly known as stacker cranes) - intended for use within narrow aisles. Upper and/or lower guidance also offers support for mast and platform;

(d)   electronically guided/free ranging - guided by an electronic guidance system while in a narrow aisle by a signal generated from a wire buried in the warehouse floor and steered by the operator when in other areas;

(e)   dedicated industry based - manufactured for and used within a specific industry, for example a whisky cask hoist.

An OPM fitted with a platform or cage on which a person is raised or lowered is considered to be a lift or hoist within the meaning of the Offices, Shops and Railway Premises (Hoists and Lifts) Regulations 1968. In particular these machines are covered by Schedule 2 of these Regulations and are required to be periodically examined by a competent person (see paragraph 193). The provision and maintenance of OPMs that are, so far as is reasonably practicable, safe and without risks to health is a requirement under Section 2 of the Health and Safety at Work etc Act 1974.

### Hazards associated with the use of OPMs

191 The following hazards exist when OPMs are used:

(a)   overturning, for example by overloading, gradients, disengagement with guides or extreme acceleration/deceleration;

(b)   falls of people, goods or materials from the platform/cage;

(c)   trapping of people in the raising, lowering or travelling mechanisms;

(d)   trapping of people between the platform/cages or other parts of the machine and fixed structures, for example racking, building walls, overhead pipework;

(e)   people being struck by a moving OPM or being trapped within racking aisles between the racking and the machine;

(f)   failure of the platform/cage supporting mechanism;

(g)   people being stranded on the platform/cage due to power failure;

(h) inadvertent movements, for example misapplication of the controls.

## Training of OPM operators

192 No person should be permitted to operate an OPM unless properly trained, competent and authorised in writing by the employer to do so, or undergoing formal training under competent supervision. It is recommended that a comparable training format to that detailed in paragraphs 165-170 is adopted.

## General safety precautions for use of OPMs

193 The following general safety precautions should be followed when OPMs are used:

(a) only properly trained and authorised persons should be permitted to operate OPMs;

(b) a safe working load notice should be conspicuously displayed on the OPM. The notice should also indicate the maximum number of people permitted on the operator's platform when in use. The safe working load notice should never be exceeded;

(c) every OPM should be tested and examined by a competent person before it is taken into use and thereafter examined by a competent person at least once every six months. A copy of the signed report of examination (Form F54) should be kept by the employer. Where any report or examination shows that the OPM cannot be used with safety the OPM should be taken out of use until remedial repair works have been carried out;

(d) suitable precautions should be provided to prevent operator access to dangerous parts of the OPM, for example mast sections, ropes, chains;

(e) The edges of the operator's platform should be provided with rails or other equally effective means of protection, comprising top rails, intermediate rails and toe boards. The height of the upper surface of the top rail above the platform shall be neither less than 900 mm nor greater than 1100 mm, the toe boards having a minimum height of 100 mm. Any gate provided should not open outwards or downwards and should be so arranged as to automatically return to the closed or fastened position, unless it is electrically interlocked to prevent motion when not in the closed position. (Further information on interlocking can be found in BS 5304:1988 - see Appendix 5);

(f) suitable overhead guards should be provided at platforms to prevent falling objects striking the operator;

(g) the OPM should be capable of being controlled from the platform. Where only one person is on the platform it is acceptable for suitable two-hand controls and safety pads for the feet to be provided to prevent access to trapping points. Controls should be:

(i) clearly marked to indicate their function and mode of operation;

(ii) of a 'hold-to-run' type (ie permits movement of the machine only as long as the control is held in a set position, returning automatically to the stop position when released); two-hand hold-to-run controls will give increased protection;

(iii) designed and installed so that unintentional operation is prevented, so far as is reasonably practicable;

(iv) designed and positioned so that the operator cannot place any part of his or her body between the moving OPM and fixed obstructions, for example racking;

(v) such that movement of the controls is in the same direction as the intended movement of the OPM;

(h) two person operated OPMs should be fitted with additional two hand 'hold-to-run' controls for the second operator. It should not be possible to move the machine unless both operators are in position at the controls;

(i) the OPM should be fitted with suitable brakes, so designed that the OPM does not become unstable when braking. A parking brake should be fitted to prevent movement of the OPM when not in operation;

(j) the OPM should be fitted with suitable 'safety gear' to prevent 'free-fall' of the platform should suspension mechanisms fail;

(k) the OPM should be provided with a device, for example a key, which prevents unauthorised use;

(l) the OPM should be provided with a clearly audible warning device. Consideration should be given to providing an audible warning device which will operate automatically during descent of the platform/cage;

(m) suitable means should be provided to enable the operator to descend safely should the operator's platform/cage jam in a raised position;

(n) stocktaking: Certain machines designed for one person only order picking operations are required to carry two people, specifically for the purposes of stocktaking. Where the design of the machine cannot intrinsically guarantee that each person is safe within the confines of the platform/cage before or while movement of the OPM takes place, further protection must be provided. The protection normally takes the form of wing guards attached to the sides of the platform. The guards should extend to a height of 2 m above the platform floor and be so arranged that the person on the platform cannot place any part of his or her body between the moving OPM and fixed obstructions such as racking.

## SCISSOR LIFTS

194 Scissor lifts can be either fixed or portable and are used to transfer goods or people from one level to another. In warehouses they are commonly used in loading areas to assist in the loading and unloading of lorries. It is recommended that scissor lifts that comply with BS 5323:1980 (see Appendix 5) are provided.

195 Scissor platform lifts that are used to transfer goods or people from one level to another are deemed to be lifts under the Offices, Shops and Railway Premises (Hoists and Lifts) Regulations 1968 and should be periodically examined by a competent person (see paragraph 192).

196 Associated hazards include:

(a) trapping of hands and feet at the closing scissor mechanism during lowering;

(b) trapping between the underside edges of the platform and the baseframe or ground during lowering;

(c) trapping of people against walls or other fixed objects;

(d) trapping of people under the platform;

(e) trapping of introduced extraneous material during raising or lowering, causing hazards to people nearby.

197 Scissor lifts should be provided with the following safeguards:

(a) clear notice fixed to it, specifying:

(i) the safe working load;

(ii) that people should not work under the platform unless it has been mechanically locked to prevent descent;

(b) aprons or other guards to enclose the trapping hazards, or a tripping device below the level of the platform which will immediately stop the platform descending should an object, for example a person's foot, be met during descent.

Note: Where scissor lifts are installed in a location to which the public have access, guarding of sufficient rigidity, for example bellows, steel mesh, sheet steel etc, should be provided to prevent access to the underside of the platform.

(c) unless the scissor lift is totally enclosed or so constructed that the scissor arms are safe by position, the minimum clearance between adjacent scissor arms should be 30 mm and the minimum horizontal clearance between the scissor arms and the platform or the base frame should be 50 mm;

(d) controls should be of a 'hold-to-run' type and be designed as detailed in paragraph 198(g)ii. An emergency stop button should be provided at ground or floor level;

(e) manually operated scotches or other equally effective means should be provided to enable the lift to be mechanically locked in a raised position when maintenance or repair work is necessary;

(f) scissor lifts used as working platforms, where the maximum height of the platform above ground or floor level exceeds 1.98 m, should be provided with suitable fencing or gates to prevent people accidentally falling from the platform. Any gate fitted should be at least 1 m in height and be so arranged to return automatically to the closed position.

## CONVEYORS

198 There are many types of conveyor system but the two commonest types found in warehouses are belt conveyors and roller conveyors.

### Belt conveyors

199 These comprise a moving belt, driven by a drum (head pulley) at one end, passing over a free-running drum (tail pulley) at the other end, the upper portion of the belt being supported by free-running idler rollers or suitable flat surfaces. This type of conveyor can be arranged for horizontal or inclined travel, the angle of slope depending on the goods conveyed and the type of belt surface.

### Roller conveyors

200 These comprise a series of moving steel rollers either free running or power driven. They can be arranged for horizontal or inclined travel.
The main hazards associated with belt and/or roller conveyors are:

(a) trapping or entanglement with transmission machinery, for example rotating shafts, couplings, chains etc;

(b) in-running nips between the belt and head and tail pulleys;

(c) trapping at the transfer point between a belt conveyor and a roller conveyor;

(d) in-running nips between the belt and return idler rollers;

(e) in-running nips between rollers of a roller conveyor;

(f) trapping between the load being carried and a fixed structure;

(g) trapping between the load being carried and rollers.

201 The following safeguards should be adopted when such conveyor systems are used:

(a) head and tail pulleys, all transmission machinery and in-running nips between belt and idler rollers should be suitably guarded to BS 5304:1988 (see Appendix 5);

(b) at the transfer point between a belt conveyor and roller conveyor provide 'jump-out' rollers (ie those that are designed as to be free to 'jump-out' should an object or part of a person's body come between the roller and moving belt - see Figure 27);

(c) power driven roller conveyors should have the following:

(i) all rollers should be power driven;

(ii) where powered and non-powered rollers are present, nip guards should be provided between rollers (see Figure 28);

(iii) each non-powered roller should be of a 'jump-out' type;

(d) suitable emergency stop arrangements should be provided, for example emergency stop buttons strategically located or a trip wire along the length of the conveyor. Emergency stop arrangements should be designed so that manual re-setting by an authorised person is necessary;

(e) a safe system of work should be established for long or complex conveyor systems to ensure that people are not exposed to any unnecessary risks, for example when a conveyor system is set in motion at the start of a working period or after an emergency stop has been used;

(f) where overhead conveyor systems are used, screening or other suitable arrangements should be provided to protect people from falling objects;

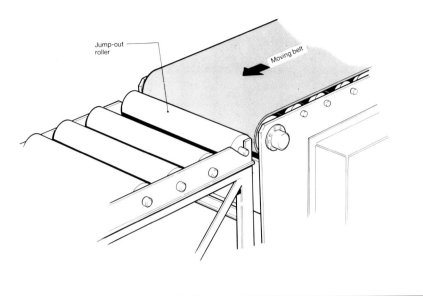

**Figure 27** Jump-out roller at transfer point between belt conveyor and roller conveyor

**Figure 28** Nip guards at roller conveyor

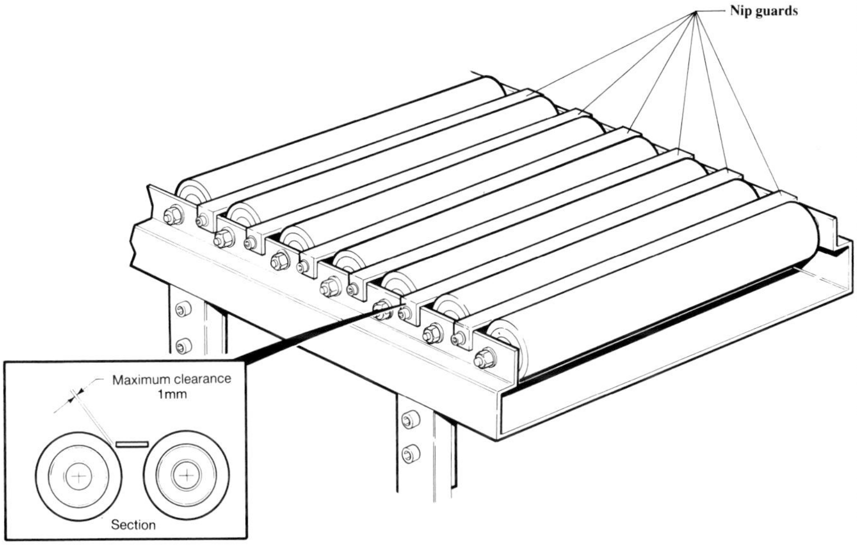

(g) riding on conveyor systems should be strictly prohibited;

## TEAGLES

202 A teagle is a loading/unloading facility comprising a fixed lifting appliance by which goods are hoisted into or discharged from a warehouse via an opening in an external wall. Teagles are frequently used in multi-floor warehouses. Accidents can occur at a teagle opening when a person may reach out to pull in a suspended load or to ease it outwards. In such circumstances the person may slip, swing outward with the load and fall.

203 The following safeguards should be provided at each teagle opening:

(a) inwardly opening doors should be fitted and kept closed and locked at all times, except when loading/unloading is taking place;

(b) secure handholds should be provided on either side of the opening. Such handholds should have their centres at about 1.2 m above floor level and have a length of grip of at least 360 mm;

(Note: chains are not acceptable as handholds)

(c) a suitable notice should be prominently displayed giving sufficient clear information about the associated hazards and the safe system of work to be adopted when loading and unloading;

(d) the safe working load of the lifting appliance should be clearly displayed.

## OVERHEAD TRAVELLING CRANES

204 Overhead travelling cranes (ie cranes comprising a bridge supported by end carriages capable of travelling along elevated tracks) are found in certain specialised storage warehouses, for example metal stockholders. The hazards and safety requirements for such equipment are complex and beyond the scope of this publication. See Appendix 5 for further references providing relevant information on the safe use of overhead travelling cranes.

## GENERAL

205 A schematic layout of one type of automated and semi-automated warehouse is shown in Figure 29. It comprises a reception point where palletised goods are placed onto mechanical handling devices, for example lift trucks, conveyors, automatic guided vehicles, and which are then taken to a transfer point where the palletised goods are transferred onto a storage and retrieval machine and placed into storage racking. The retrieval of palletised goods from the storage racking is the reverse procedure.

206 In an automated warehouse the movement of goods is carried out by a computer controlled storage and retrieval machine. In a semi-automated warehouse the storage and retrieval machine is rider-operated, the operator receiving information from a computer via an on board visual display device.

## HAZARDS

207 Hazards include those between reception and transfer points. For hazards associated with lift trucks and conveyor systems see Manual Handling section.

## AUTOMATIC GUIDED VEHICLES (AGVS)

208 AGVs may be used to transfer goods from reception to transfer point. AGVs normally operate at about walking speed and are commonly controlled and guided by a wire-guidance system whereby the AGV follows a low-voltage signal carried in a wire buried below the floor surface.

209 The hazards associated with the use of AGVs include:

(a) collision between AGVs and people;
(b) trapping points between AGVs and stationary objects or fixed structures;
(c) dangerous occurrences by inadvertent movement of the AGV, for example where AGVs interact with storage and retrieval machines the AGV could move off before the load transfer is complete, causing displacement or collapse of the load or other devices.

210 Hazards at transfer points include:

(a) trapping points between mechanical handling devices, palletised loads and the structure of transfer point;

(b) collapse of palletised load;

(c) trapping points between automated storage retrieval machine, palletised load, mechanical handling devices and the structure of transfer point.

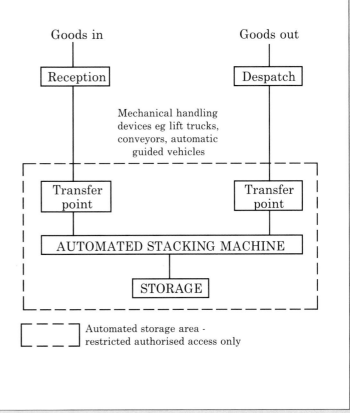

**Figure 29** Schematic layout of an automated warehouse

Goods in       Goods out

Reception       Despatch

Mechanical handling devices eg lift trucks, conveyors, automatic guided vehicles

Transfer point       Transfer point

AUTOMATED STACKING MACHINE

STORAGE

Automated storage area - restricted authorised access only

211 Hazards in an automated storage area include:

(a) being struck by automated storage and retrieval machine;

(b) trapping points between automated storage and retrieval machines and fixed structures, for example racking;

(c) trapping points between dangerous moving parts of the automated storage and retrieval machine;

(d) trapping points at transfer points for goods, for example transfer arms, transfer pallets;

(e) trapping points at transfer points for automated storage and retrieval machines which serve more than one aisle (movement of stacker onto transfer bogey, movement of the transfer bogey);

(f) collapse of an automated storage and retrieval machine or load;

(g) fall of load (due to, for example, mislocation of load);

(h) overrun of automated storage machine in horizontal or vertical travel;

(i) inadvertent movement of an automated storage and retrieval machine.

## HAZARD ANALYSIS AND RISK ASSESSMENT

212 To ensure that people are adequately safeguarded the system should be subjected to a hazard analysis, followed by an assessment of the risk. Hazard analysis should include a detailed and systematic scrutiny of all actions and events that may take place in the automated system to identify dangerous events. It should include those occurring during normal use and also under foreseeable fault conditions. Risk assessment should include a prediction of the likelihood of people being injured by the hazards identified, balanced with the potential severity of the injury. This will enable a judgement to be made about which safeguards should be adopted.

213 Because of the complexity of most automated systems it is recommended that the techniques of hazard analysis and risk assessment be applied to the design of the installation and its systems at an early stage. Such assessments should be included in the design of any Programmable Electronic System (PES). Further advice and information may be obtained from the HSE booklets, *PESs in safety related applications* (vols 1 and 2 - see Appendix 5).

## SAFEGUARDING AUTOMATED AND SEMI-AUTOMATED SYSTEMS

214 The type of hazard created and the level of risk will determine which safeguard(s) are appropriate. BS 5304 (see Appendix 5) gives further information on safeguarding methods, the assessment of risk, and how to select an appropriate safeguard for that level of risk. Further advice on the principles of safeguarding relevant to automated systems can be found in the HSE publication *Industrial robot safety* (see Appendix 5).

215 It is not implied that the only suitable safeguards are those described here, but any alternative means should be demonstrably at least as safe and reliable as the appropriate conventional safeguarding method.

### Between reception and transfer points

216 Safeguards for lift trucks and conveyor systems are described in the Manual Handling section. Where AGVs are used safeguards include:

(a) segregation of AGV operating areas from pedestrian traffic;

(b) provision of trip devices in the direction of travel of the vehicle, such as front and rear bumpers, which will stop the movements of the AGV if depressed; trip devices should be designed with flexible bumpers to ensure that

the vehicle stops before the object touching the bumper is reached by the main structure of the vehicle;

(c) provision of trip whiskers, probes or optical devices along the sides which will stop the vehicle when activated;

(d) means to slow the AGV from full to crawl speed should an obstacle be detected in its path (for example ultrasonic or optical sensors);

(e) means to ensure accurate positioning of the AGV at transfer points;

(f) emergency stop buttons on the vehicle accessible from any side;

(g) automatic monitoring of the safety system; this includes automatic monitoring of the machine condition, for example brakes and sensors, so that the main computer can arrange to take suitable action, for example an emergency stop, should a system failure occur;

(h) audible and visual signals to indicate that the vehicle is moving or about to move or that an obstacle has been detected.

### At transfer points

217 In automated and semi-automated warehousing the palletised load is transferred from the mechanical handling device to the automated storage and retrieval machine, usually via an opening in the perimeter fence surrounding the storage area. Risks may arise from: contact with dangerous moving parts of the transfer mechanism; and access into the restricted area of the warehouse through large openings for feeding and delivery of pallets.

218 Dangerous moving parts of the transfer mechanism should be dealt with by, as far as possible, eliminating them by design, by providing close guarding, for example for chains and sprockets, vee belt drives, and by fixed or interlocked guards. The use of electro-sensitive safety systems, including pressure sensitive mats and photo-electric devices (see paragraphs 219-222) may be necessary either to supplement fixed or interlocked guarding, or instead of such guarding if it is not practicable. Access through the feed and delivery openings into the restricted area of the automated warehouse should be prevented by the following:

(a) restricting the size of the opening to the minimum possible, for example when trays of components are being fed into the system. This may present a simple and effective way of preventing access. Secondary traps between the load and sides of the fixed opening should, however, be avoided. It may be necessary to provide sensitive edges or trip flaps at the openings to prevent finger traps;

(b) if it is not possible to reduce the opening to the extent that a person is not able to climb through, other means will be required, for example a photo-electric safety device which causes a shut-down of the transfer system and those parts of the automated warehouse which would be accessible following access through the opening. This PE system would be muted after positive identification of the presence of incoming or outgoing goods for a timed period to allow goods in/out. Means of identification include a combination of transponders, identification tags, pallet profile identification, patterns and sequences of tripping of photo-electric sensors, load sensors etc.

The objective should be to allow legitimate goods entry and egress, but to prevent human access to an automated storage area when it is in operation.

219 Examples of safety systems include:

(a) *electro-sensitive safety systems*. These systems may be arranged to operate as trip devices, on the principle of detecting the approach of people or as presence-sensing devices where dangerous parts cannot be set in motion when a person or object is detected. BS 6491 (see Appendix 5) gives information on the specification for the design and testing of electro-sensitive safety systems;

(b) *photo-electric (PE) safety systems*. These systems operate on the principle of the detection of an obstruction in the path taken by a beam or beams of light (visible or invisible, for example infra-red). Recommendations for the design and performance of high integrity photo-electric safety systems are given in BS 6491 and guidance on their application is given in HSE Guidance Note *Application of photo-electric safety systems to machinery* (see Appendix 5).

220 They may be used as:

(a) a trip device;

(b) a presence-sensing device;

(c) a combination or zoning system where two or more PE devices are used as sensors and/or trip devices.

### Pressure sensitive mats

221 These devices are placed on and secured to the floor with a sensitive upper surface so that the pressure applied by a person standing on them will cause dangerous motion to stop.

222 The use of electro-sensitive safety systems, PE safety systems, pressure sensitive mats or other suitable safeguards should be such that the presence of a person or people in an identified and defined hazardous area will be detected and the appropriate action taken to remove or reduce the risk of injury, for example conveyor system stopped and approach to the automated stacking machine prevented.

### Storage area

223 Safeguards for storage areas include:

(a) conventional perimeter fencing, made from rigid panels 2 metres high, securely fastened to the floor or to some convenient structure, for example racking, and positioned so that it is not possible to reach any dangerous parts of machinery or trapping points between automated stacking machines and fixed structures;

(b) access gates provided with interlocking device(s), for example a trapped key exchange which positively isolates the power supply or the control to all or parts of the storage system. The essential elements are a lock on the gate(s) in the perimeter fencing and another lock on the control unit for the automated stacking machine. The key cannot be removed from the control unit to open the gate lock until a safe condition is established, for example isolation of the power supply to automated stacking machine;

(c) safe systems of work. It is particularly important to establish a safe system of work, for example for routine maintenance work, access for statutory examination of plant and where the automated stacking machine is rider-operated. It is important that the design of the system allows safe systems of work to be adopted. (Hence the importance of detailed discussions between the supplier and user of the system.) If it is necessary to restore power to the system with a person inside the restricted area, for example for fault finding, fault recovery or maintenance, there should be means to enable this to be done in safety which should embody the following principles:

(i) restoration of power to the system should be in the hands of the person within the restricted area, for example key exchange system which allows the person within the restricted area to restore power to a specific stacking machine);

(ii) operation of the stacking machine or other unit should be under the sole control of the person within the restricted area. There should be no other possibility of restoring automatic operation, and the stacking machine or other item of equipment should not respond to remote signals;

(iii) all other equipment should remain isolated. Alternatively, if there are multiple bays and several stacking machines, there should be means of safely isolating the stacking machine in the bay being worked on to prevent transfer bogies or other machines moving into that bay and to prevent maintenance staff moving into operating areas. The effective means should include software control features, hardware features and physical barriers;

(iv) there should be a safe place or places of work for the person within the restricted area, for example areas around the subsidiary control panel (if any), working platform on the stacking machine etc;

(v) access/egress routes to rider-operated stacking machines should be designed so that entry into other parts of the restricted area, for example aisles, is not possible. For example access gate cannot be opened until stacking machine is stationary and in a precise location to allow safe access/egress.

A safe system of work should comprise a carefully considered analysis of the hazards, taking into account all the modes of operation, the needs for access/approach, leading to the formulation of a method of working which will ensure the safety of those engaged in the particular activity. For each activity involving access to automated storage areas a formal written safe system of work should be adopted. In some situations, for example repair work, it may be necessary to introduce a formal permit-to-work system which should set out:

(i) a clear hand-over procedure;
(ii) what work is to be done;
(iii) who is to carry it out and the equipment necessary for the task;
(iv) what safety precautions are to be taken;
(v) a clear hand-back procedure;

(d) effective means should be provided to prevent overrun in the horizontal and vertical directions of travel, and to ensure the stacking machine is correctly positioned for loading, unloading and stacking etc. An adequate combination of limit switches and position-sensing devices should be provided and clearly identified in maintenance manuals etc. As a final safeguard, buffers should be provided on track-mounted systems at the limits of horizontal travel;

(e) the safeguards described in paragraph 193 should be adopted for rider-operated stacking machines. In particular, increased protection will be achieved if a two-handed 'hold-to-run' control is combined with a sensor fitted to the operators seat such that the operator must be seated with both hands on the controls before the stacking machine can be operated;

(f) clear, unambiguous warning notices should be prominently displayed at all access gates and strategic locations. Such notices may include:

(i) Restricted access. Authorised persons only.

(ii) Authorised persons must have read and understood the written safe systems of work.

(iii) Procedures specified in the safe system of work must be strictly adhered to.

224 The movement of goods and materials into, out of and around warehouse premises involves the use of a wide range of vehicles and accounts for a large proportion of accidents in warehouses. It is important, therefore, for the employer to devise a safe system of traffic management. Such a system should include methods and procedures for arrival, reception, unloading, loading and movement within the curtilage of the premises. The system should be written down and brought to the attention of all people involved or likely to be involved in such activities, for example employees, visiting drivers, and, where necessary, other visitors. It is particularly important that upon arrival, for example at the security house or entrance gate, visiting drivers are made aware of the procedures for unloading/loading and movement within the premises. Clear unambiguous information signs setting out these procedures should be prominently displayed at the entrance and other strategic locations. The issue of information/instruction cards to visiting drivers upon arrival may help to improve awareness.

## ROAD SYSTEMS

225 The following safeguards should be considered:

(a) roadways should be wide enough for the safe movement of the largest vehicle liable to use them;

(b) the need for vehicles to reverse should be minimised as far as possible, for example by the use of one-way traffic systems or designated areas;

(c) sharp bends and blind corners should be avoided. Where they are unavoidable the use of suitable warning signs and the provision of suitably placed mirrors may help to reduce danger;

(d) entrances and gateways should be of sufficient width and there should be enough space to accommodate vehicles stopped for checking, without causing obstruction either within the premises or on the public highway;

(e) road surfaces should be constructed of tarmacadam, concrete or other suitable material. They should have even surfaces and be properly drained. Excessive gradients should be avoided as far as possible, particularly where lift trucks are likely to operate. Steep gradients should be properly signed;

(f) road surfaces should be properly maintained and, in particular, pot holes should not be allowed to develop;

(g) all roads should be adequately lit;

(h) vulnerable items of plant, for example bulk LPG storage tanks, should not be located adjacent to or in close proximity to roads. Where this is unavoidable, suitable vehicular protection should be provided;

(i) suitable and sufficient designated parking areas should be provided to allow the segregation of private cars from goods traffic;

(j) realistic speed limits should be in operation and should be enforced. Speed limit signs should be displayed at strategic locations. Where necessary to reduce the speed of vehicles, speed retarders (road humps), together with suitable prominent warning notices, should be provided. Note: Road humps are unsuitable for use in lift truck operating areas. See Manual Handling section;

(k) sufficient clear road and direction signs should be provided. The marking of buildings and strategic locations will help to avoid unnecessary traffic movements. All signs should comply with the Safety Signs Regulations 1980. Where appropriate, road traffic signs should be of the design prescribed by the Traffic Signs Regulations and General Directions Regulations 1981 and set out in the Highway Code for use on public highways.

## PEDESTRIAN MOVEMENT

226 Separate specific routes should be provided for pedestrians. Routes should include, where appropriate:

(a) designated and clearly marked crossing places;

(b) suitable barriers or guardrails at entrances to and exits from buildings;

(c) a separate route for pedestrians, so far as is reasonably practicable, where vehicles pass through doorways see (Figure 30); all such doorways should be provided with vision panels and be clearly and conspicuously marked with the safe clearance height.

## PROTECTION OF PEDESTRIANS WORKING WITH VEHICLES

227 The following safeguards should be adopted when pedestrians are working with, or adjacent to, vehicles:

(a) members of the public and non-essential employees, for example office staff, should not be permitted into areas where vehicles are moving or being loaded/unloaded;

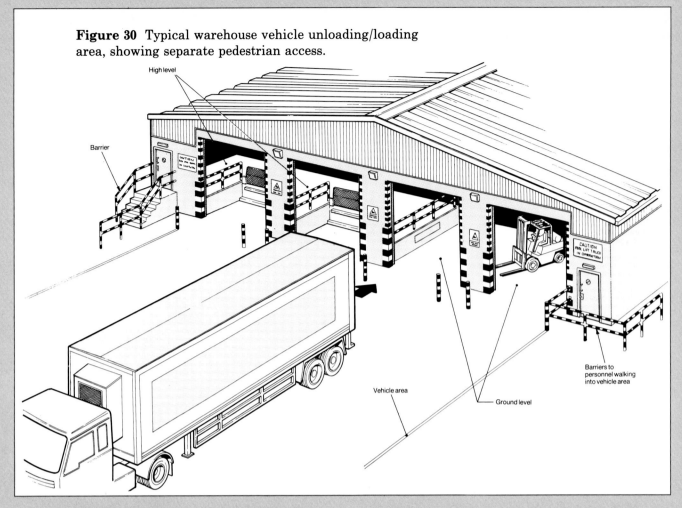

**Figure 30** Typical warehouse vehicle unloading/loading area, showing separate pedestrian access.

High level

Barrier

Barriers to personnel walking into vehicle area

Vehicle area

Ground level

(b) provide sufficient clear and unambiguous warning signs at strategic locations to inform people that vehicles operate in this area;

(c) instruct all essential employees to stand clear when vehicles are moving or being loaded/unloaded by mechanical handling devices, for example lift truck, overhead travelling crane;

(d) provide and instruct essential employees to wear British Standard safety footwear (BS 1870 - see Appendix 5), and where there is a foreseeable risk of head injury from falling objects, safety helmets (to BS 5240 - see Appendix 5). A further useful precaution would be the provision of high visibility clothing or light coloured overalls.

228 Provide loading bays with at least one exit, and wide loading bays with at least two exit points, one at each end. If it is not possible for those loading bays constructed before 1 January 1993 (Workplace (Health, Safety and Welfare) Regulations 1992) to be provided with such exit points, a refuge should be provided where a person will not be liable to be struck or crushed by a vehicle. A designated reception/waiting area for lorry drivers should be considered.

229 Where a vehicle is being loaded or unloaded close to the driver's cab, there is a risk of injury from goods or materials collapsing onto the cab or the mechanical handling device piercing the cab,

for example forks of an LT. In such circumstances the lorry driver should not be permitted to remain in the driver's cab and should be instructed to use the reception/waiting area where provided, or instructed to stand in an area which does not place him or her in a vulnerable position.

230 When loading or unloading takes place the lorry driver may need to issue instructions, for example to the LT driver, regarding positioning of loads. In such circumstances a safe system of work should be adopted to ensure that the lorry driver is not placed in a vulnerable position. Where it is not necessary for the lorry driver to assist in loading/unloading he or she should be instructed to use the reception/waiting area, where provided, or to remain in the cab of the vehicle, unless there is a risk from doing so (see paragraph 229).

**REVERSING VEHICLES**

231 When vehicles reverse a significant hazard is that of people being knocked down or trapped between the vehicle and fixed structures. The risks associated with the reversing of vehicles may be reduced by the following:

(a) providing an employee to guide the vehicle while it is reversing. Such a person should be properly trained and competent to guide reversing vehicles without placing themselves or others in danger. A clear, unambiguous system of signalling should be employed, for example a system recommended by the Road

Transport Industry Training Board in their booklet *Reverse and safety signals for guidance of drivers* (see Appendix 5). The position taken up by the signaller will depend upon the circumstances under which reversing is carried out. The signaller should never stand between the rear of the reversing vehicle and fixed structures. A person standing well clear, using a mobile communication system with the driver, is an alternative, improved method to guide reversing vehicles;

(b) where it is impracticable for a vehicle to be guided backwards and the driver does not have adequate rear vision, the area behind the vehicle should be checked to ensure it is clear before reversing and that, so far as is reasonably practicable, it stays clear;

(c) provision of longitudinal guides, white lines on the floor or fixed mirrors to aid reversing;

(d) fitting audible warning devices to vehicles, arranged to operate when the vehicle reverses;

(e) fitting audible/visible warning devices at loading bays, arranged to operate when the vehicle reverses.

## PREMATURE VEHICLE DEPARTURE

232 A particular hazard at loading bays is that of a vehicle accidentally driving away during loading/ unloading, causing lift trucks or other mechanical handling devices and/or people to fall from the vehicle or loading dock. Such an occurrence can lead to serious injuries and it is therefore essential to establish a safe system of work for loading and unloading and departure of vehicles.

233 Safe systems of work may include:

(a) a properly managed and supervised procedure, for example where the keys to the vehicle and/ or necessary paperwork for the journey are not given to the driver until it has been confirmed that the vehicle is ready for departure;

(b) the use of suitable vehicle/trailer restraints, whereby the vehicle/trailer is firmly held to the loading dock by a hook or other suitable device, which is effectively secured to the loading dock or other fixed structure;

(c) the provision of a suitable traffic light system, for example in multibays where detached trailers are standing awaiting connection to the tractor unit;

(d) competent supervisory controls including the use of a marshalling person(s).

## STABILITY OF SEMI-TRAILERS

234 When uncoupled from the trailer unit a semi-trailer needs support at its front end. This is usually provided by a pair of 'landing legs'. The legs are usually lowered or raised by manual winding with a handle attached to a drive shaft. As loading or unloading of an uncoupled semi-trailer progresses, the distribution of load changes. The shorter trailers may approach the point where they become balanced about the landing legs or front heavy if the load is not evenly distributed. This may cause the trailer to 'nose-dive' or cause collapse of the landing legs, particularly if a lift truck is driven on and off. To reduce the risks arising during loading and unloading the use of safety jacks or other suitable support should be considered (suitable proprietary jacks are available). Semi-trailers should not be uncoupled or loaded/unloaded on soft or rough ground. The semi-trailer handbrake should always be applied before it is uncoupled from the tractor unit. As an additional precaution the wheels of the trailer should be chocked.

## LOADING AND UNLOADING

235 The following practices should be followed wherever possible:

(a) no vehicle should be loaded beyond its rated capacity or beyond the legal limit of gross weight;

(b) before loading is started, the floor of the vehicle should be checked to ensure that it is safe to load;

(c) loads should be properly secured or arranged so that they are safe for both transportation and unloading, for example so that they do not slide forward in the event of the driver having to brake suddenly, or move sideways when cornering;

(d) loading/unloading should be carried out so as to maintain, as far as possible, a uniform distribution of the load. Uneven loading may result in the vehicle or trailer becoming unstable, particularly if it is an articulated or similar type of trailer which has been detached from the tractor unit (see paragraph 234).

(e) loading and unloading vehicles from one side using lift trucks can result in pallets on the opposite side being disturbed sufficiently to cause a pallet(s) to fall. The opposite curtain or side should be retained in position while loading/unloading;

(f) before ropes, tarpaulins or the curtains of curtainsider lorries are removed, the vehicle and load should be checked to ensure that the removal of ropes or other security devices will not allow materials or goods to fall;

(g) the driver of the vehicle is responsible for ensuring that the load is secure: operators of lift trucks should take instructions from the driver concerning positioning of loads;

(h) loading/unloading should never be carried out on significant gradients.

236 When an opening or edge is being used to load/ unload goods or materials from one level to another, where there is a danger of a person falling, it should be fenced as far as possible. If fencing is not possible, alternative safeguards should be used as far as possible, for example a secure guard rail which goods or materials may safely pass under or over. Detailed information on the safety of vehicle loads is given in the *Department of Transport Code of Practice Safety of loads on vehicles* (see Appendix 5).

## DOCK LEVELLERS

237 Dock levellers are devices used to bridge the gap between the loading dock and vehicle trailer, thereby providing access for lift trucks and roll containers etc. There are two basic types:

(a) hydraulic - raised and lowered by an electrically powered hydraulic cylinder;

(b) mechanical - activated by a pull chain or other device that releases a spring mechanism, raising the platform and extending the lip. The platform descends into its working position on the trailer bed when an employee 'walks down' the platform.

238 The main hazards associated with dock levellers are:

(a) trapping of feet or toes between the descending platform and loading dock;

(b) overturning of mechanical handling devices (for example by contact with raised or depressed platform);

(c) trips or falls caused by raised or depressed platform;

(d) falls of people, goods or materials from platform.

(e) trapping of people underneath dock leveller.

239 The following safeguards should be adopted when dock levellers are used:

(a) when dock levellers, which are installed as an integral part of the loading dock, are not in use and people, lift trucks, roll containers or other mechanical handling devices are likely to travel over or adjacent to the dock leveller, its platform should be returned to a horizontal position flush with the loading dock as soon as

loading/unloading is completed. A mechanism fitted to the dock leveller which automatically returns the platform to a horizontal position after use will give increased protection against the risks caused by inadvertent raised or depressed platform positions;

(b) toe guards should be provided, for example fencing at the sides of the leveller that prevent feet or toes from being caught under the platform as it descends - BS 5304:1988 (see Appendix 5) gives detailed information on safeguarding methods;

(c) provide a mechanism which prevents the springs from pulling back the platform to its raised position during loading/unloading on mechanical dock levellers (this will prevent the risk of a lift truck reversing into the raised platform when leaving the trailer);

(d) provide a mechanism which prevents the platform from free-falling in the event of an emergency, for example premature departure of a vehicle (see paragraphs 232-233).

(e) provide skirt plates or other suitable devices to enclose the trapping hazards below the platform;

(f) provide manually operated scotches or other equally effective means to enable the dock leveller to be mechanically locked in a raised position when maintenance or repair work is necessary.

## MAINTENANCE

240 Defective dock leveller safety features, twisted, cracked or misaligned platforms or other defects can cause serious accidents, for example overturning of lift trucks. Employers should therefore have:

(a) an effective system to report defects and carry out remedial repair work;

(b) a planned routine maintenance system.

## TAIL LIFTS

241 Tail lifts (ie lifts, fitted to a vehicle, which enable a load-carrying platform to be raised and lowered) are commonly used in warehouses for loading and unloading vehicles. Two common types are:

(a) column lifts - the lifting platform runs vertically between guides fixed to the vehicle body;

(b) cantilever lifts - the lifting platform is raised and lowered by hydraulic rams and a series of linkages so that the platform moves horizontally and vertically.

242 The main hazards associated with tail lifts are:

(a) trapping of feet or toes between the moving platform and ground or stationary parts of the vehicle or lift;

(b) trapping of fingers or parts of the body by moving mechanisms;

(c) trapping of people under the platform;

(d) crushing of people by unsecured loads falling or rolling on or off the platform;

(e) falling of people from the platform.

## SAFEGUARDS

243 Tail lifts should be designed and installed in accordance with BS 6109 and BS 5304 (see Appendix 5). In particular, safeguards include the following:

(a) provision of 'hold-to-run' controls, ie movement of the lift platform can only take place while the controls are being operated, the controls returning automatically to the 'off' position when released. All controls should be:

 (i) designed to prevent accidental operation;

 (ii) clearly marked to indicate the direction of movement;

 (iii) so sited that the operator has a clear view of the platform throughout its travel.

(b) elimination of finger and toe traps within the mechanism by providing a minimum gap of 75 mm between the platform and any fixed part of the vehicle except at those points where adequate toe protection is provided. Examples of adequate toe protection can be found in Appendix C of BS 6109. Where it is impracticable to provide minimum safety gaps, for example on some types of cantilever lift, tripping devices are an acceptable alternative;

(c) where the tail lift platform height exceeds 2 metres above floor or ground level:

 (i) effectively secured grab rails should be provided at both sides of the vehicle aperture, so positioned as to be conveniently held by people working above 2 metres from the floor or ground level;

 (ii) it should have suitable fixings for guard rails on the three sides remote from the vehicle;

 (iii) guard rails or other equally effective means, to a height of at least one metre should be provided for use at the tail lift platform;

 (iv) a notice should be affixed adjacent to the controls, advising on the following points:

• fitting of guardrails;

• that care is needed when standing near an unguarded opening or edge;

• the desirability of pushing (as opposed to pulling) loads from the vehicle onto the platform;

• the importance of preventing loads from rolling, sliding or tipping;

(d) every tail lift should be thoroughly examined by a competent person at least once in every period of 12 months and a report of the result of every such examination should be signed by the person making the examination (where chains or ropes are fitted the inspection should be carried out every six months). The report should detail any repairs, renewals or alterations required to enable the tail lift to continue to be used with safety, specifying whether such work is required immediately or within a specified time;

(e) proper maintenance and lubrication should be carried out in accordance with the manufacturer's instructions;

(f) all tail lifts should be clearly marked with the safe working load, the manufacturer's name and address, the type, serial number and year of manufacture. The safe working load should never be exceeded;

(g) under no circumstances should vehicles be driven with a loaded tail lift platform;

(h) before travelling, the platform should be checked to ensure that it is securely fastened in the stowed position.

## GENERAL

244 Cold stores operate at various temperatures below freezing, according to the requirements of individual products. Air temperatures can be as low as minus 30°C and, in exceptional cases, lower. (The Quick Frozen Foodstuffs Regulations 1990 require that certain specified types of foodstuff be kept at minus 18°C or lower). The hazards associated with this harsh environment include:

(a) *Accidental locking-in*. This is potentially a very serious hazard which can lead to fatal accidents;

(b) *Accidental release of refrigerant*. (Refrigerants can be classified into three main groups - see Table 7). Equipment failure, improper maintenance work, or mechanical damage to refrigeration plant, particularly in compressor rooms, may lead to the release of refrigerant, for example ammonia which is toxic and flammable or halocarbons which, although of a low order of toxicity, can displace oxygen and cause suffocation in confined spaces or produce toxic decomposition products;

(c) *Cold injury*. Freezing of the tissues results in frostnip or frostbite. Prolonged cold exposure, without freezing, may cause chilblains;

(d) *Increased risk of accidents*. Low temperatures may cause slower mental reactions and reduce manual skills which may increase the risk of accidents;

(e) *Special medical risks*. People suffering from certain medical conditions including chronic respiratory disease, asthma, cardiovascular disease and arthritis may be particularly vulnerable to low temperatures (see Appendix 4 for details);

(f) *Ice build up*. Ice build-up may occur on the floor, above and around entrance doors and other places when warm moist air enters the cold store. When the door(s) is open, the moisture in the air quickly condenses and freezes onto the nearest cold surface. If not regularly removed, ice deposits can lead to serious accidents should they fall onto a person below, or cause floors to be uneven and slippery. Frozen spillages on the floor can present slipping and tripping hazards for people and skidding and overturning hazards, where mechanical handling devices are used;

(g) *Increased risk of equipment failure*. Racking structures, lift trucks and other mechanical handling devices which operate permanently in the cold store may require more frequent inspection and maintenance to identify and remedy defects caused by continual exposure to low temperatures. Careful selection of equipment should reduce this problem to a minimum.

## SAFEGUARDS AND PRECAUTIONS

245 The following safeguards should be adopted when operating a cold store:

(a) the design, construction and installation of the refrigeration system should be in accordance with BS 4434;

(b) *precautions against accidental locking-in*:

(i) Only authorised people should be allowed to enter the cold store. Such people should be fully instructed on the means of escape, the use of 'locked-door' opening devices and trapped-man alarms.

(ii) Clear, conspicuous signs should be prominently displayed at the entrance door(s), indicating 'No unauthorised entry'.

(iii) At least one emergency exit should be provided. The employer should, however, make an assessment as to whether additional emergency exits are required. Such exits should be suitably positioned with due regard for the operational layout and should not be obstructed by racking, stock or equipment. Such exits should be adequately signed with either emergency lighting or luminous signs located in such a position as not to be obstructed by racking, stock or equipment. Clear illuminated instructions on the method of escape should be marked on the emergency exit. Emergency exit doors should be capable of being opened from the inside at all times (in some cases it may be necessary to fit local strip heaters). It is recommended that *all* doors at new cold stores be installed so that they can be opened from the inside even when padlocked from the outside.

(iv) A trapped-man alarm, mains operated, with battery back-up, should be provided. The call point should be located no higher than 900 mm above the floor of the cold store and be suitably marked (illuminated or luminous sign) to indicate its position and function. The alarm should be distinctive sounding, for example clearly distinguishable from the fire alarm and the sounding device located in an area that is normally manned.

(v)   Battery-operated emergency lighting to BS 5266: Part 1 (see Appendix 5) should be provided to indicate clearly and unambiguously the escape route(s).

(vi)  Trapped-man alarms, door release devices and emergency exits should be properly maintained and regularly tested to ensure that they are in good working order.

(vii) Before a cold store is locked a thorough check should be made by an appointed member of staff to ensure that it is unoccupied.

(viii) The Fire Authority should be contacted for advice regarding any arrangements or conditions that may be necessary to meet current fire safety standards. Where fire exits are required, these are likely to be adequate for the purposes of paragraph b(iii).

(c)  *Precautions against accidental release of refrigerant*

(i)    All refrigeration plant should be properly maintained by a person(s) who is properly trained and competent.

(ii)   All people involved in the operation of the plant should be properly trained and competent.

(iii)  Many refrigeration plants, for example those having a maximum operating power exceeding 25 kW, will be subject to the requirements of the Pressure Systems and Transportable Gas Containers Regulations 1989 and the Approved Code of Practice (see Appendix 5). A particular requirement of the Regulations is for the user of a refrigeration system to have a written scheme for the periodic examination, by a competent person, of all protective devices, every pressure vessel and pipeline and those parts of the pipework in which a defect may give rise to danger.

(iv)  A clear emergency procedure including details of the precise duties of all relevant staff and the arrangements for evacuation, rescue, first aid, plant isolation etc should be drawn up and effectively communicated to everyone likely to be effected in an emergency situation.

(v)   Plant rooms should be provided with adequate and suitable ventilation including:

•  adequate ventilation to prevent build-up of toxic or dangerous concentrations of refrigerant from operational leakage. Mechanical ventilation should be provided in plant rooms housing systems of groups 2 and 3 refrigerants (see Table 7);

•  emergency ventilation to prevent dangerous accumulations of a refrigerant, for example

flammable ammonia vapour/air mixtures) in the event of a reasonably foreseeable plant or operational failure, for example valve failure;

•  refrigerant vapour detectors should be provided in plant rooms to activate an alarm and to automatically switch on the ventilation fans;

(vi) *Group 1 refrigerants*. Ventilation fans should switch on if the concentration of refrigerant exceeds the occupational exposure limits (see HSE Guidance Note EH 40 *Occupational Exposure Limits* - see Appendix 5);

(vii) *Group 2 refrigerants*. Ventilation fans should switch on if the concentration of refrigerant exceeds 1% (V/V);

(viii) *Group 3 refrigerants*. Ventilation fans should switch on if the concentration of refrigerant exceeds 25% of the lower explosive limit.

•  In unmanned machinery rooms for groups 2 and 3 refrigerants, the detector(s) should also isolate all  unprotected electrical circuits, other than emergency  lighting and ventilation, by circuit breakers located in a safe place.

•  The refrigerant concentration in each plant room should be monitored at one or more points within the room and detectors should be positioned to give warning of any leakage before a dangerous vapour accumulation can occur.

•  The refrigerant detector when sensing a refrigerant concentration exceeding its pre-set limit should, in addition to its other functions, initiate an alarm in the plant room and also elsewhere so that emergency action may be initiated.

•  Electrical equipment likely to operate in flammable concentrations of refrigerant should comply with the requirements for hazardous (potentially explosive) areas (see BS 5345, BS 4683, and BS 5501 - see Appendix 5).

•  Where refrigerant vapour is likely to be present at a significant level, self-contained or airline breathing apparatus should be provided at suitable locations together with adequate instructions on its correct use, for example for rescue or fault-finding purposes.  All such equipment should be suitable for its purpose and conform to an HSE approved standard or be type approved by HSE.  Breathing apparatus should be thoroughly examined and tested at least once a month (see the Control of Substances Hazardous to Health Regulations 1988).  All personnel likely to be involved in such operations should be effectively trained in the correct use and wearing of such equipment. Safe systems of work should be adopted. Further information can be found in HSE Guidance Note GS 5 *Entry into confined spaces*.

(d) *Working at low temperatures*

(i) Special arrangements should be made for welfare of personnel who are exposed to low temperatures for extended periods. These will include the provision of thermal/protective clothing (see paragraph e(i)). Warm rooms with a hot drinks dispenser, that employees may use during breaks, may also be required. Suitable and sufficient breaks should be arranged for cold store operators so that they may warm themselves. Experience has shown that workers suffering physical discomfort after a period of work in a cold store may require approximately 20 minutes at 20°C with their outer clothing removed in order to fully recover. The length and frequency of breaks will depend on the nature of the work, the working temperature and exposure time.

(ii) Where lift trucks operate inside the cold store for the duration of the shift, heated, enclosed driver's cabs should normally be provided.

(e) *Protective clothing*

(i) Protective clothing of suitable quality should be provided to protect against low temperatures. Selection of suitable clothing should take into account the temperature, length of exposure and personal preference. Different considerations will apply, for example to extended working periods compared to intermittent or short-term exposure.

(ii) Examples of protective clothing are as:

- undergarments - thermal quality;
- socks and/or boot liners;
- outer clothing - one-piece insulated suits or jacket and trousers or in some instances, thigh-length insulated coats;
- head covering ranging from balaclava helmets to bump caps to insulated safety helmets;
- gloves or mittens;
- insulated boots;

(iii) Several thin layers of clothing are better than one thick layer in providing insulation. Activity in cold weather can quickly cause sweating. Water must be allowed to escape if sweating is not to wet the clothing. If water does not escape properly, heat loss from

the body can occur when activity stops, causing a refrigeration effect in addition to discomfort for the wearer. Clothing worn next to the skin should have good 'wicking' properties. Polypropylene is more suitable than cotton. Nylon is least suitable. All fabrics lose their insulating properties when wet. The clothing system should be designed to keep the inner garments dry both from the inside and the outside.

(iv) Suitable facilities should be provided for drying wet or damp clothing. Clothing should be laundered according to the manufacturer's instructions to ensure that it does not lose its thermal properties.

(v) Selection of protective footwear will require careful consideration. In some situations, footwear may be needed that is both insulated against low temperature and resistant to impact. Standard safety footwear, with steel toe-caps, may be unsuitable for extended exposure to lower temperatures. Safety footwear with high impact resistant plastic toe-caps, suitably insulated, may provide the degree of protection needed. Information about suitable clothing for specific working conditions may be obtained from manufacturers and suppliers.

(f) *Precautions against special medical risks.* People working in cold stores should be physically capable of undertaking the work and be free from any disability likely to be adversely affected by the low temperature. A pre-employment medical examination is recommended and thereafter at regular intervals, if specified by an occupational physician or following significant sickness leave (see Appendix 4 for details).

(g) *Ice build up.* All ice build-up, for example above entrance doors, and frozen spillages should be removed on a regular basis, for example daily, to prevent the risk of injury to from falling ice or slipping, tripping or overturning or skidding of mechanical handling devices.

(h) *Equipment failure.* The manufacturers of all equipment used at low temperatures, for example lift trucks, racking systems, should be consulted for advice on special hazards that may exist and the necessary precautions that may be required to be taken to reduce risks associated with the use at low temperatures.

**Table 7** Group classification of refrigerants

| Group | Refrigerant characteristics | Examples |
|---|---|---|
| 1 | Refrigerants which are non-flammable in vapour form at any concentration in air at atmospheric pressure and 20°C and are of a low order of toxicity.<br><br>Toxic decomposition products may result from contact with flames or hot surfaces in the presence of air. Major decomposition products of this group, with the exception of carbon dioxide, are hydrochloric and hydrofluoric acid. Although toxic, they provide an automatic and definite warning by their exceedingly irritant smell, even at low concentrations. | Halocarbons (eg Dichlorodifluoro-methane (R12) and Monochlorodifluoro-methane (R22) |
| 2 | Refrigerants which have toxicity as a dominant characteristic. It is almost impossible to make a functioning refrigerating system that would not produce toxic concentrations if the refrigerant escaped into the spaces concerned. | Ammonia |
| 3 | Refrigerants which have flammability or explosion hazards as their dominant characteristics.<br>They are of a low order of toxicity. | Ethane, propane, butane, isobutane, ethylene, propylene |

## GENERAL

246 The storage of packaged dangerous substances in substantial quantities may create serious risks, not only to people working at the warehouse but also to the general public in the area and to the environment. The precautions needed to achieve a reasonable standard of control should take into account the properties of the substances to be stored. Different substances create very different risks and it is important that the standards adopted at the warehouse are based on an understanding of the physical and chemical properties of the substances concerned. Other important factors are the overall quantities of the substances to be stored and the maximum size of individual packages.

247 At all warehouses where packaged dangerous substances are to be stored the employer should, before undertaking such storage, consider the risks created and the means adopted to control such risks, under the categories of:

(a) identification and assessment;

(b) prevention and control;

(c) mitigation of risk.

248 It is recommended that the means adopted to control risks from the storage of dangerous packaged substances be written into the company safety policy. A periodic review of these matters should be carried out, particularly if storage conditions change.

## IDENTIFICATION AND ASSESSMENT

### Information

249 The hazards of packaged dangerous substances should be identified by discussion and/or correspondence with the supplier before being accepted for storage. Manufacturers and suppliers have a legal duty to provide adequate information about any risks to health or safety to which the inherent properties of a dangerous substance may give rise and about any conditions necessary to ensure that the substance will be safe and without risks to health when it is being used, handled, stored or transported. The information provided should refer to an internationally recognised

classification system for dangerous substances. Most dangerous substances arriving at the warehouse will be marked with CPL (The Classification, Packaging and Labelling of Dangerous Substances Regulations 1984) conveyance labelling, but goods in international transit may be marked using the similar but more comprehensive UN (United Nations) scheme. (Appendix A of the HSE booklet HS(G) 71 *Storage of packaged dangerous substances* (see Appendix 5) sets out the various categories of dangerous substance with a brief description of their properties and illustrates the conveyance labels).

### Actions pre-arrival on-site

250 Some substances will require special conditions for storage (see Appendix A and paragraph 23 of HS(G)71) which should be clearly identified in advance, for example segregation. Substances requiring special conditions should only be accepted for storage when the required conditions can be made available at the warehouse.

### Actions on arrival

251 On arrival, the contents of each consignment or individual package should be checked, identified and assessed against the shipment documents to verify acceptability. A check should also be made against records detailing what the supplier said would be sent to avoid a situation where an employee checking the goods confirms they are what the lorry driver's ticket says they are, but is at the same time unaware that his or her employer did not agree to receive those goods in the first place. Dangerous substances should usually be identifiable by the conveyance labelling attached to the outer layer(s) of the packaging and for most purposes can be assessed accordingly. The additional information obtained from the manufacturers and suppliers may identify specific examples of non-compatibility, and storage location should take account of this.

252 If the contents of any package are not immediately identifiable, it should not be sent to store. Such packages should be held only for the minimum time necessary to obtain information, or the supplier should be required to have them removed from the site promptly.

253 Once the storage location for a consignment has been allocated, a physical check should be made to confirm that adjacent materials are those shown on stock records. If all or part of a consignment is moved during its period of storage, the check procedures should be repeated to ensure that the new storage location will still be valid.

## PREVENTION AND CONTROL STRATEGY

### Package integrity

254 The primary protection against the dangers arising from storing dangerous substances is the integrity of the packaging. Individual containers may leak, break or be punctured, causing a small escape of material, and arrangements should be in place to deal with this eventuality. Much greater risks arise where a large number of containers fail in a short time and the principal means by which this may occur is fire.

### Segregation

255 Often the first material ignited in a fire is not itself a dangerous substance. For this reason, stocks of combustible materials such as easily ignitable packaging should not be kept in storerooms with dangerous substances. Separate storage areas should be provided. Similarly, even small quantities of dangerous substances stored in a warehouse for general goods may seriously increase the consequences of any fire, and in particular add to the dangers for the fire brigade. Dangerous substances should preferably be stored in dedicated compartments of the warehouse which are effectively fire-separated from the rest of the building.

256 The intensity of a fire, or its rate of growth, may be increased if incompatible materials are stored together. In addition, a fire may grow and involve dangerous substances which of themselves are not combustible. In this way toxic materials may be widely dispersed. To prevent this type of escalation a system of segregation is necessary in a warehouse storing dangerous substances. (Further information on segregation can be found in paragraph 23 of the HSE booklet HS(G)71.)

### Ignition sources

257 All possible sources of ignition, for example smoking, maintenance work, electrical power supplies, arson, heating systems, warehouse vehicles and battery charging facilities, should be strictly controlled.

### Handling

258 All packages containing dangerous substances should be handled carefully to avoid damage to the containers, or spillage of the contents. Damaged or leaking containers should not be placed in store, but should be repacked or disposed of safely in accordance with arrangements made with, or information provided by, the supplier. Repacking should be carried out in an area remote from the main storage areas (see Occupational Health section).

### Stock control

259 Storerooms and compounds should not be overstocked, and permanent instructions should specify a maximum storage capacity for each location. Gangways should be kept clear of obstructions, especially those designated as means of escape. At least 1 m of clear space should be left between all stock tops and the warehouse roof, roof beams or light fittings. Where sprinklers are fitted, spacing should be in accordance with the design code for the system. This information should be available from the system installers.

260 Where a number of different types of dangerous substance are stored, a comprehensive record of stocks, providing details of the quantity, nature and exact location of all dangerous substances in a store, should be made and carefully updated each time a stock movement occurs. A copy of the records should be kept available at a point on the site that is unlikely to be affected in an emergency, so that they can be used by both management and the emergency services when dealing with an incident.

### Storage stability

261 Some types of materials may degrade or become unstable during prolonged storage. These should be identified by information supplied by the supplier or the manufacturer. Maximum recommended storage times should not be exceeded and this should be achieved by careful stock rotation. The advice of the supplier should be sought if material is found which has reached, or is about to reach, the recommended latest storage date.

262 Any stock held for a prolonged period should be inspected at intervals to detect any damaged or degrading packaging.

## SPILLAGES

263 The employer should ensure that there is a safe system of work to deal with spillages (see Occupational Health section). When dealing with spillages, all non-essential or untrained staff should be evacuated.

### Liquid spillages

264 Where liquids are stored, methods for containing spillage should be provided. Barrier materials such as sand bags or proprietary absorbent granules are recommended, depending on the nature of the substance and the quantities involved.

### Solid spillages

265 Spillages of dangerous substances in a fine dusty form should not be cleared up by dry brushing. Vacuum cleaners should be used in preference, and, for toxic materials, one conforming to type H of BS 5415 should be used.

### Personal protection

266 Protective clothing and equipment will be necessary for dealing with accidental releases of dangerous substances. Protective footwear, gloves and eye protection are likely to be the minimum requirements. In some cases additional items will be needed, for example respiratory protective equipment.

267 When corrosive materials have been spilt, care should be taken to ensure that clothing with the necessary resistance is worn by people dealing with the spillage. Clothing contaminated with any dangerous substance should be removed immediately. Spare overalls should be available on site. Contaminated clothing should not be sent with other general laundry, nor taken home. It may be cleaned by arrangement with a specialist laundry, or disposed of as dangerous waste.

## WARNING SIGNS

268 Warning notices or signs should be posted at entrances to a warehouse storing dangerous substances. Where 25 tonnes or more of dangerous substances are stored, the Dangerous Substances (Notification and Marking of Sites) Regulations 1990 make specific requirements for posting hazard warning signs and the design of signs used. The fire brigade should be consulted about requirements for the siting of signs.

269 Further comprehensive information can be found in the HSE booklet *Storage of packaged dangerous substances* - see Appendix 5).

## MANAGEMENT AND TRAINING

270 A senior member of staff should be appointed by the employer to be directly responsible for the identification, assessment, handling and safe storage of all dangerous substances on site. The person appointed should have suitable qualifications, training and experience. Written operating procedures should be adopted covering matters such as selection of storage locations, dealing with spillages and security arrangements. This person should be familiar with the legislation relevant to the activities undertaken, and be responsible for liaising with the enforcing authorities and the emergency services.

271 Employees should be trained to recognise and understand the risks associated with the particular classes of dangerous substances that will be kept in the warehouse. They should be shown how to understand the system of labelling adopted under the CPL Regulations (see Appendix 5). They should also be told where particular substances should be stored and why, and should be made familiar with the precautions and safety procedures adopted by the warehouse.

272 Instructions for dealing with an emergency should include the steps necessary to enable staff to identify easily and deal with damaged and/or leaking packages and containers. Training should be given in the use of safety equipment provided and in the actions to be taken in the event of fire. Any Fire Certificate in force will normally specify requirements for this.

## SPECIAL REGULATIONS

### Control of Industrial Major Accident Hazards (CIMAH) Regulations 1984

273 For the small number of warehouses storing dangerous substances on a sufficient scale to exceed the threshold quantities determining application of the top tier of the CIMAH Regulations, a safety report will have to be prepared and submitted to HSE's Area Office. The report will have to cover all matters set out in Schedule 6 to the Regulations. On-site emergency plans will have to be prepared and technical information supplied to the Council's Emergency Planning Officer so that an off-site plan can be prepared. In England and Wales, the County, London Borough or Metropolitan District Councils are responsible. In Scotland, the Regional or Islands Councils are responsible. Information will also have to be supplied to the public who might be affected by a major accident about the nature of the hazards and the behaviour they should adopt. Storage which would cause top tier CIMAH to apply for the first time should not commence until three months after the safety report has been submitted. Extensions of the scope of storage beyond the limits set in the safety report should be similarly preceded by a revised report. Full details of the requirements and the scope of application are contained in the HSE booklet *A guide to the Control of Industrial Major Accident Hazards Regulations 1984.*

### Pesticide storage

274 The Control of Pesticides Regulations 1986 made under the Food and Environment Protection Act 1985 require pesticides to be approved before they may be advertised, sold, supplied or stored. In addition, sites storing more than 200 kg or 200 litres of a pesticide approved for agricultural use must be stored under the control of a person holding a

recognised Certificate of Competence. The MAFF *Code of practice for suppliers of pesticides to agriculture, horticulture and forestry* (see Appendix 5) sets out standards required.

275 From 1 April 1992 local authorities will enforce the Control of Pesticides Regulations in warehouses where the Local Authority is the enforcing authority (see Appendix 1).

# APPENDIX 1: ENFORCING AUTHORITIES

1   Local authorities (LAs) are responsible for inspection and enforcement in warehouses where the main activity is the sale or storage of goods for retail or wholesale distribution.

2   For the main activity to be storage for retail or wholesale distribution it is not necessary for the goods to be distributed by the occupiers of those premises.

3   The LA will normally be responsible for enforcement in respect of metal stockholders and timber merchants.

4   Excluded from LA enforcement and included within the jurisdiction of HSE are warehouses where the main activity is:

(a) storage as a service, for example furniture depositories;

(b) storage of raw materials, components or part finished goods intended for further processing;

(c) storage at manufacturers' warehouses in which finished goods await transfer to the distribution chain;

(d) sale or storage by a company whose business is that of a transport undertaking; transport undertakings are limited to those which themselves carry the goods and would not include, for example, mail order firms who use agents to deliver;

(e) storage at container depots in the course of transit to or from dock premises, an airport or a railway;

(f) sale or storage for wholesale distribution of dangerous substances; dangerous substances are defined in Regulation 2(1) of the Classification, Packaging and Labelling of Dangerous Substances Regulations 1984 (see Appendix 5).

5   HSE has enforcement responsibility for any installations to which the top tier of the Control of Major Accident Hazards (CIMAH) Regulations 1984 apply.  If such an installation forms only part of a warehousing site, the LA will have enforcement responsibility for the rest of the site.

6   Where allocation is unclear, for example the contents of a warehouse regularly change to include dangerous substances, either HSE or the

LA can be assigned as the enforcing authority.  Notice of such an assignment will be given in writing to the employer.

7   It is essential to ascertain the enforcing authority for your particular warehouse so that the details can be either stated on the approved poster and displayed on the premises or given to each employee with the approved leaflet *Health and Safety Law: What you should know* (see Appendix 5).  If in doubt contact your LA Environmental Health Department or local HSE Area Office for advice.

APPENDIX 1

64

Listed below are typical routine electrical checks
for portable apparatus, to be carried out by a
suitably competent person.

Note: This checklist is intended as a guide; certain apparatus may
need different or additional electrical inspections and tests. Non-
electrical checks are outside the scope of this booklet.

Equipment:
Make:
Serial No:

| Item | Test | Pass condition |
|---|---|---|
| 1 mains lead | (a) visual inspection no damage | two layers of insulation and BS colours |
| | (b) mains plug correct fuse fitted | correctly connected cable clamp gripped to sheath |
| 2 *either:* mains lead instrument connector (if lead detachable) | (a) visual inspection of panel male connector | BS type or equivalent |
| | (b) attempt to open socket without tool | unopenable |
| | (c) attempt to pull cable from female connector | no movement |
| *or:* grommet/clamp protected | (a) inspection of grommet | cable insulation protected |
| | (b) sharp pull on cable | no appreciable movement |
| | (c) rotation of cable | no rotation |
| 3 mains on/off switch | (a) visual inspection | correct operation no damage |
| *either 4 or 5* 4 conducting case | (a) visual inspection: (if marked □ treat as item 5) | |
| | Earth tester which will check resistance and pass a current of at least twice the fuse rating | earth resistence 0.1 ohms or earth resistence 0.5 ohms for loads fused at 3 A or less |
| | (b) high voltage insulation 500 V ac no fault indicated minimum test | no fault indicated after 5 s |
| 5 insulating case | visual inspection | maker's double insulation mark □ visible case undamaged |
| 6 accessible fuse holders | visual inspection | no damage removal of carrier does not permit live* part to be touched |
| 7 exposed output connections | (a) visual inspection | no voltage greater than 50 V |
| | (b) for outputs greater than 50 V, test short-circuit current | short-circuit current less than 5 mA |

\* ie live at more than 50 volts when in use

Overall result (Delete as necessary)
Unit is - passed
       - failed

Signed ............................................... Date .........................................

## 1 Hazard diamonds

| Classification | Hazard warning sign |
| --- | --- |

Explosive substances
Class 1

Non-flammable compressed gas
Class 2.2

Flammable liquid
Class 3

Spontaneously combustible substance
Class 4.2

Oxidising substance
Class 5.1

Toxic substance
Class 6.1

Harmful substance
Class 6.1

Flammable gas
Class 2.1

Toxic gas
Class 2.3

Flammable solid
Class 4.1

A substance which in contact with water emits flammable gas
Class 4.3

Organic peroxide
Class 5.2

Corrosive substance
Class 3

Other dangerous substance
Class 9

APPENDIX 3

66

# 2 User hazard warnings

| Classification and indication of general nature of risk | Symbol<br>Black symbol on orange background |
| --- | --- |
| Very toxic |  |
| Toxic |  |
| Harmful |  |
| Corrosive |  |
| Explosive |  |
| Oxidising |  |
| Extremely flammable and highly flammable |  |
| Irritant |  |

1    Cold exposure causes physiological effects which may be harmful to those with cardiovascular disease.  Cold air inhalation may precipitate an asthmatic episode.  A history of local cold injury may predispose an individual to a subsequent attack.  Particular care should be given to assessment of the following conditions:

- cardiac disease;
- hypertension;
- peripheral vascular disease;
- respiratory disease;
- thyroid or other endocrine disease;
- rheumatic or musculoskeletal disorders.

2    Many prescribed drugs and alcohol may impair thermoregulation in the cold.  These include anti-depressants, tranquillisers, hypnotics, drugs of abuse, hypoglycaemics, anti-thyroid drugs and sympathetic and ganglion blocking agents.

3    Where a medical examination is performed a full clinical examination should be made.  Special tests such as electro-cardiography or lung function testing should be undertaken at the discretion of the occupational physician.

4    Detailed advice on medical assessment of fitness for work can be found in *Fitness for Work: The Medical Aspects* edited by Edwards, McCallum and Taylor, Oxford University Press 1988 ISBN 0 19 261774 5.

# APPENDIX 5: FURTHER INFORMATION SOURCES

## ORGANISING HEALTH AND SAFETY

### General

*Essentials of Health and Safety at Work* (rev)
HMSO 1990 ISBN 0 11 8854453 3

### Law

*HSW ACT: The Act Outlined* HSC 2 1975 Free

*HSW ACT: Advice To Employers* HSC 3 1975 Free

*HSW ACT: Advice To Employees* HSC 5 1975 Free

*Writing a safety policy statement: advice to employers* HSC 6 1987 Free

*Regulations, approved codes of practice and guidance literature* HSC 7 1976 Free

*Safety committees: guidance to employers whose employees are not members of recognised trade unions* HSC 8 1976 Free

*HSW ACT: Your obligations to non-employees* HSC 11 1985

*Short guide to the employers' Liability (Compulsory Insurance) Act 1969* HSE 4 (rev) 1991 Free

*Don't wait until an inspector calls... the law on health and safety at work: essential facts for small businesses and the self employed* HSE 16 1986 Free

*A Guide To The HSW Act 1974* L1 (4th ed) HMSO 1990 ISBN 0 11 885555 7

*Securing compliance with health and safety legislation at work: how it is done and how it affects you* IND(G)14(L) 1983 Free

*Guide To The OSRP Act 1963* HSR(R)4 (rev) HMSO 1989 ISBN 0 11 885463 1

*Health And Safety Law: What You Should Know* (poster) HMSO 1984 ISBN 0 11 701424 9

*Health And Safety Law: What You Should Know* (leaflet) HMSO 1989 ISBN 0 11 701425 7

*Writing your health and safety policy statement: guide to preparing a safety policy statement for small businesses* HMSO (rev) 1989 ISBN 0 11 885510 7

### Accidents and emergencies

*First aid needs in your workplace: your questions answered* IND(G) 3(L) 1990 Free

*First aid at work: general guidance for inclusion in first-aid boxes* IND(G) 4  HMSO 1987 ISBN 0 11 883958 6

*Reporting an injury or a dangerous occurrence* HSE 11 1986 Free

*Reporting a case of disease* HSE 17 1986 Free

*First aid at work* HS(R) 11 HMSO 1981 ISBN 0 11 883446 0

*Guide to Reporting of Injuries, Diseases and Dangerous Occurrences Regulations 1985* HS(R) 23 HMSO 1986 ISBN 0 11 883858 X

*First Aid At Work: Health and Safety (First Aid) Regulations 1981 and Guidance* COP 42 HMSO 1990 ISBN 0 11 885530 1

### General working environment

*Watch Your Step* IND(G) 32(L) 1983 Free

*Do your signs comply? The Safety Signs Regulations 1980* IND(G) 33(L) 1985 Free

*Lighting at work* HS(G) 38 HMSO 1987 ISBN 0 11 883964 0

*Assessment of fire hazards from solid materials and the precautions required for their safe storage and use* HS(G) 64 HMSO 1991 ISBN 0 11 885654 5

*A Guide to the Safety Signs Regulations 1980* HS(R) 7  HMSO 1981 ISBN 0 11 883415 0

*Watch your step: prevention of tripping, slipping and falling accidents at work* HMSO 1983 ISBN 0 11 883782 6

*Ventilation of Workplaces*  EH 22 (rev) HMSO 1988 ISBN 0 11 885403 8

*Floor loading in warehouses - review*  Building Research Establishment 1987 BRE report no 284 ISBN 0 85 125247 8

*Asbestos materials in buildings* (3rd ed) Department of the Environment 1991 HMSO ISBN 0 11 752370 4

BS 5266 *Emergency lighting* 1988

BS 5378 ( in three parts) *Safety signs and colours*

### Personal Protective Equipment

BS 1651 *Specification for industrial gloves* 1986

BS 1870 ( in three parts) *Safety footwear*

BS 2092 *Specification for industrial eye protectors* 1987

BS 5240 *Industrial safety helmets* 1987

BS 6344 (in three parts) *Industrial hearing protectors*

BS 6476 *Guide to garment quality and relevant British Standards* 1991

BS 6629 *Specification for optical performance of high visibility garments* 1985

*Respiratory protective equipment: legislative requirements and lists of HSE approved standards and type of approved equipment* (3rd ed) HMSO 1992 ISBN 0 11 886382 7

## ELECTRICAL SAFETY

*Guidance for small businesses on electricity at work* IND(G) 89(L) 1990 Free

*Protection against electric shock* HSE Guidance Note GS 27 HMSO 1984 ISBN 0 11 883583 1

*Flexible leads, plugs, sockets etc* HSE Guidance Note GS 37 HMSO 1985 ISBN 0 11 883519 X

*Electricity at work: safe working practices* HS(G)85 (in preparation)

*Electrical hazards from steam/water pressure cleaners etc* PM 29 (rev) HMSO 1988 ISBN 0 11 883538 6

*The safe use of portable electrical apparatus* PM 32 (rev) HMSO 1990 ISBN 0 11 885590 5

*Electrical apparatus for use in potentially explosive atmospheres* HS(G) 22 HMSO 1984 ISBN 0 11 883746 X

*Memorandum of guidance on the Electricity At Work Regulations 1989* HS(R) 25 HMSO 1989 ISBN 0 11 883963 2

BS 196 *Specification for protected-type non-reversible plugs, socket outlets, cable-couplers and appliance-couplers, with earthing contacts for single phase ac circuits* 1961

BS 4293 *Specification for residual current operated circuit-breakers* 1983

BS 4343 *Specification for industrial plugs, socket-outlets and couplers for ac and dc supplies* 1968

BS 4683 (in four parts) *Specification for electrical apparatus for explosive atmospheres*

BS 5345 (in eight parts) *Code of practice for selection, installation and maintenance of electrical apparatus for use in potentially explosive atmospheres (other than mining applications or explosive processing and manufacture)*

BS 5420 *Specification for degrees of protection of enclosures of switchgear and controlgear for voltages up to and including 1000 V ac and 1200 V ac* 1988

BS 5501 (in nine parts) *Electrical apparatus for potentially explosive atmospheres*

BS 6467 (in two parts) *Electrical apparatus with protection by enclosure for use in the presence of combustible dusts*

BS 7071 *Specification for portable residual current devices* 1989

*IEE Wiring Regulations: Regulations for electrical installations* (16th ed) Institution of Electrical Engineers 1991 ISBN 0 852965 10 9

*Classification of degrees of protection provided by enclosures* (2nd ed) IEC 529 Institute of Electrical Engineers 1993

## OCCUPATIONAL HEALTH

### Hazardous substances

*Occupational skin diseases: health and safety precautions* EH 26 HMSO 1981 ISBN 0 11 883374 X

*Occupational exposure limits* EH 40 (revised annually) HMSO ISBN 0 11 885696 0

*Dust in the workplace: general principles of protection* EH 44 (2nd ed) HMSO 1991 ISBN 0 11 885595 6

*Respiratory protective equipment: a practical guide for users* HS(G) 53 HMSO 1990 ISBN 0 11 885522 0

*Respiratory protective equipment: legislative requirements and lists of HSE approved standards and type of approved equipment* (3rd ed) HMSO ISBN 0 11 886382 7

*Save your skin: occupational contact dermatitis* MS(B) 6 1987 Free

*Down with dust* IND(G) 60L 1989 Free

*COSHH - a brief guide for employers* IND(G)136L Free (in preparation)

*An introduction to the Employment Medical Advisory Service* HSE 5 (rev) 1990 Free

*Approved Codes of Practice: Control of Substances Hazardous to Health* L5 (3rd ed) HMSO 1982 ISBN 0 11 885698 7 (formerly COP 29)

*Approved Code of Practice: Control of lead at work* COP 2 HMSO 1985 ISBN 0 11 883780 X

*Approved Code of Practice: Control of asbestos at work* COP 21 HMSO 1988 ISBN 0 11 883984 5

*Noise at work (Noise Guides 1 & 2) The Noise at Work Regulations 1989* HMSO 1989 ISBN 0 11 885512 3

*Noise assessment, information and control (Noise Guides 3-8)* L3 (formerly HS(G) 56) HMSO 1990 ISBN 0 11 885430 5

*100 practical applications of noise reduction methods* HMSO 1983 ISBN 0 11 883691 9

*Introducing the Noise at Work Regulations* IND(G) 75(L) 1989 Free

*Noise at Work: leaflet for employees* IND(G) 99(L) 1991 Free

## Upper limb disorders

*Work related upper limb disorders: a guide to prevention* HS(G) 60 HMSO 1990 ISBN 0 11 885565 4

*Health aspects of job placement and rehabilitation - advice to employees* MS 23 HMSO 1989 ISBN 0 11 885419 4

*Ergonomics at work* IND(G) 90(L) 1990 Free

*Fitness for work: The medical aspects* Oxford University Press 1988 ISBN 0 19 261774 5

## PLANT AND EQUIPMENT

### General

BS 3810 (in nine parts) *Glossary of terms used in materials handling*

### Pallets

*Safety in the use of timber pallets* PM15 HMSO 1978 ISBN 0 11 883186 0

BS 2629 (in three parts) *Specification for pallets for materials handling for through transit*

BS 6407 (in two parts) *Cage pallets for retail use*

### Racking

*Recommended practices for the use of static racking* (5th ed) Storage Equipment Manufacturers Association (SEMA) 1989

### Ladders

*Safe use of ladders, step ladders and trestles* GS 31 HMSO 1984 ISBN 0 11 883594 7

BS 1129 *Specification for portable timber ladders, steps, trestles and lightweight stagings* 1990

BS 2037 *Specification for portable aluminium ladders, steps, trestles and lightweight stagings* 1990

### Lift trucks

*Safety in working with lift trucks* HS(G) 6 HMSO 1979 ISBN 0 11 883284 0

*Rider operated lift trucks - operator training: Approved Code of Practice and supplementary guidance* COP 26 HMSO 1988 ISBN 0 11 885459 3

*Working platforms on forklift trucks* PM 28 HMSO 1981 ISBN 0 11 883392 8

*Diesel engined lift trucks in hazardous areas* PM 58 HMSO 1986 ISBN 0 11 883535 1

### Refuelling

*Keeping of LPG in cylinders and similar containers* CS 4 HMSO 1986 ISBN 0 11 883539 4

*Automatic LPG Refuelling Facilities* Liquefied Petroleum Gas Industry Association (LPGITA) Code of Practice 20 1984 ISBN 0 90032365 5

*Safety of pressure systems* COP 37 HMSO 1990 ISBN 0 11 885514 X

Safety of transportable gas containers COP 38
HMSO 1990 ISBN 0 11 885515 8

Storage of LPG at fixed installations HS(G) 34
HMSO 1987 ISBN 0 11 883908 X

The storage of flammable liquids in fixed tanks (up
to 10 000 m³ total capacity) HS(G) 50 HMSO 1990
ISBN 0 11 885532 8

The storage of flammable liquids in containers
HS(G) 51 HMSO 1990 ISBN 0 11 885533 6

## Overhead travelling cranes

Safe working with overhead travelling cranes PM 55
HMSO 1985 ISBN 0 11 883524 6

Training of crane drivers and slingers GS 39 HMSO
1986 ISBN 0 11 883932 2

BS 7121 (in two parts) Codes of practice for the safe
use of cranes

BS 466 Specification for power driven overhead
travelling cranes 1984

Accident control manual for overhead travelling
cranes British Steel Corporation 1973

Notes of guidance on the safety aspects of electronic
overhead travelling cranes (2nd ed) Electricity
Council 1983

## Automated systems

BS 5304 Code of Practice for Safety of machinery
1988

BS 5667 (in nineteen parts) Specification for
continuous mechanical handling equipment - safety
requirements

BS 6491 (Part 2) Specification for particular
requirements for an electro sensitive safety system
incorporating a photoelectric sensing unit(s) 1987

Industrial robot safety HS(G) 43 HMSO 1988
ISBN 0 11 883999 3

Programmable Electronic Systems Volume 1:
Introductory Guide HMSO 1987
ISBN 0 11 883913 6

Programmable Electronic Systems Volume 2: General
technical guidelines HMSO 1987 ISBN 0 11 883906 3

Photo-electric safety systems PM 23 HMSO 1981
ISBN 0 11 883384 7

Application of photo-electric safety systems to
machinery PM 41 HMSO 1984
ISBN 0 11 883593 9

### Scissor lifts

BS 5323 Code of practice for scissor lifts 1980

### Tail lifts

BS 6109 Code of Practice for tail lifts

## VEHICULAR OPERATIONS

Safety of loads on vehicles (2nd ed) Dept of
Transport Code of practice HMSO 1984
ISBN 0 11 550666 7

Reverse and safety signals for guidance of drivers
Road Transport Industry Training Board

Road transport in factories GS 9 (rev) HMSO 1992
ISBN 0 11 885732 0

BS 5323 Code of practice for scissor lifts 1980

BS 6109 Code of practice for tail lifts 1981

The Safety Sign Regulations 1980 SI 1980 no 1471
HMSO 1980 ISBN 0 11 007471 8

The Traffic Sign Regulations and General
Directions Regulations 1981 SI 1981 no 859
HMSO 1981 ISBN 0 11 016859 3

## COLD STORES

BS 4434 Specification for safety aspects in the
design, construction and installation of refrigerating
appliances and systems 1989

Entry into confined spaces GS 5 HMSO 1977
ISBN 0 11 883067 8

A guide to the Pressure Systems and Transportable
Gas Containers Regulations 1989 HS(R)30 HMSO
ISBN 0 11 885516 6

The Pressure Systems and Transportable Gas
Containers Regulations 1989 SI 1989 no 2169 HMSO
1989 ISBN 0 11 098169 3

Safety of Pressure Systems. Pressure Systems and
Transportable Gas Containers Regulations 1989
Approved Code of Practice COP 37 HMSO 1990
ISBN 0 11 885514 X

The Control of Substances Hazardous to Health
Regulations 1988 SI 1988 no 1657 HMSO 1988
ISBN 0 11 087657 1

*Control of Substances Hazardous to Health and Control of Carcinogenic Substances. Control of Substances Hazardous to Health Regulations 1988* Approved Codes of Practice 3rd ed L5 HMSO 1991 ISBN 0 11 885698 7

*The Classification, Packaging and Labelling of Dangerous Substances Regulations 1984* SI 1984 no 1244 HMSO 1984 ISBN 0 11 047244 6

*Classification and Labelling of Dangerous Substances for Conveyance by Road in Tankers, Tank Containers and Packages. Dangerous Substances (Conveyance by Road in Road Tankers and Tank Containers) Regulations 1981. Classification, Packaging and Labelling of Dangerous Substances Regulations 1984. Road Traffic (Carriage of Dangerous Substances in Packages etc.) Regulations 1986* Approved Code of Practice COP 19 HMSO 1990 ISBN 0 11 885518 2

## PACKAGED AND DANGEROUS SUBSTANCES

*Storage of packaged dangerous substances* HS(G)71 HMSO 1992 ISBN 0 11 885989 7

*A guide to the control of Industrial Major Accident Hazards Regulations 1984* HS(R)21 HMSO 1990 ISBN 0 11 885579 4

*Code of practice for the operational provisions for the Road Traffic (Carriage of Dangerous Substances in Packages etc) Regulations 1986* COP 17 HMSO 1987 ISBN 0 11 883898 9

*Classification and labelling of dangerous substances for conveyance by road in tankers* COP 19 (rev) HMSO 1990 ISBN 0 11 885518 2

BS 5415 *Specification for type H industrial vacuum cleaners for dusts hazardous to health* 1986

*Code of practice for suppliers of pesticides to agriculture, horticulture and forestry* Ministry of Agriculture, Fisheries and Food COP PB00 1990

All titles quoted are HSE publications unless otherwise stated. Priced items are available from HMSO (see back cover).
Free items are available from:
HSE Information Centre
Broad Lane
Sheffield S3 7HQ
Tel: 0742 892345
Fax: 0742 892333
Freeleaflet Line: 0742 892346

British Standards are available from:
British Standards Institution
Linford Wood
Milton Keynes
MK14 6LE
Tel: 0908 220022
Fax: 0908 320856

APPENDIX 5

74

Printed in the United Kingdom for HSE, published by HMSO C250 12/92